LEVEL B

HIGH NOON
Vocabulary

Reproducible Lessons

MICHAEL MILONE, PhD

Available from High Noon Books

High Noon Vocabulary Program

Level A   ISBN 1-57128-332-3
             Order #8332-3
Level B   **ISBN 1-57128-333-1**
             Order #8333-1
Level C   ISBN 1-57128-334-X
             Order #8334-X
Level D   ISBN 1-57128-335-8
             Order #8335-8

Editor: Deb Akers
Book Design: Bonni Gatter

High Noon Books
A division of Academic Therapy Publications
20 Commercial Boulevard
Novato, CA 94949
800-422-7249

International Standard Book Number 1-57128-333-1

15 14 13 12 11 10 09 08 07 06
10 09 08 07 06 05 04 03 02 01

Order #8333-1

TABLE OF CONTENTS

INTRODUCTION

ACTIVITIES

INTRODUCTION

As an element of reading with understanding, vocabulary comprises two skills: decoding a word and understanding its meaning. It is these two skills on which *High Noon Vocabulary* focuses. This focus serves a purpose beyond simply enriching the vocabulary of the students who use *High Noon Vocabulary*. By learning to decode printed words in text and understanding the meaning of the words, students will be more likely to read fluently and comprehend what they read.

The philosophy that underlies *High Noon Vocabulary* is consistent with The Report of the National Reading Panel (2000). "Vocabulary occupies an important position in learning to read. As a learner begins to read, reading vocabulary encountered in texts is mapped onto the oral vocabulary the learner brings to the task. That is, the reader is taught to translate the (relatively) unfamiliar words in print into speech, with the expectation that the speech forms will be easier to comprehend. A benefit in understanding text by applying letter-sound correspondences to printed material only comes about if the resultant oral representation is a known word in the learner's oral vocabulary. If the resultant oral vocabulary item is not in the learner's vocabulary, it will not be better understood than it was in print. Thus, vocabulary seems to occupy an important middle ground in learning to read. Oral vocabulary is a key to learning to make the transition from oral to written forms, whereas reading vocabulary is crucial to the comprehension processes of a skilled reader."

Unlike many vocabulary instruction programs, *High Noon Vocabulary* is intended for students who are reading at least one year below grade level. These students may experience a variety of reading difficulties, but the result is the same. They are struggling to read grade-level text either aloud or silently with comprehension. The sequence of words and the learning activities in *High Noon Vocabulary* are designed to meet the needs of these students.

CHOOSING THE RIGHT LEVEL OF *HIGH NOON VOCABULARY*

There are four levels of *High Noon Vocabulary*. The sound/spellings featured in each level are summarized below.

Level A – short vowels, regular consonants, blends, digraphs

Level B – review level A, silent letters, r-controlled vowels, vowel patterns, inflectional endings

Level C – digraphs, ending patterns, compound words, short and long vowel spelling patterns, prefixes, suffixes, homophones,

Level D – vowel patterns, prefixes, suffixes, multisyllable words, homophones, homographs, schwa

The words within each level and among the four levels are *not* arranged by traditional difficulty, which is typically measured by how frequently words appear in printed material. This means that both simple and challenging words are featured in every lesson. The oral interaction that is the heart of every lesson reinforces students' knowledge of words they may have heard and makes it possible for them to learn the meanings of difficult words they would not encounter in typical reading. Even older students will find decodable words like *bog* challenging because they are heard so infrequently.

In order to choose the correct level for your students, use the following guidelines. Do not rely upon a student's age or grade placement. Your own estimate of a student's reading ability is a more useful basis on which to make the decision. If you have a question about the appropriate level, choose the lower level. Even older students will find the words in the lower levels of *High Noon Vocabulary* challenging. As an example, the words *ban*, *gap*, and *nab* appear in Lesson 1 of Level A. Although these words are easily decoded, they are considered to be fifth grade words or higher.

Choose Level A if the student:
- hesitates when decoding words like *din, vile, drench*
- is unsure of or does not know meaning of words like *sag, plume, broth*

Choose Level B if the student:

- hesitates when decoding words like *quake, knead, hoisted*
- is unsure of or does not know meaning of words like *gourd, plight, bawled*

Choose Level C if the student:

- hesitates when decoding words like *clench, splendid, requirement*
- is unsure of or does not know meaning of words like *dreadful, immerse, scarlet*

Choose Level D if the student:

- hesitates when decoding words like *prior, emphasize, moisture*
- is unsure of or does not know meaning of words like *uncommon, salvage, legitimate*

It is important to recognize that *High Noon Vocabulary* is intended for a specific group of students, those who are reading significantly below grade level in grades three and higher. This group may include some students with special needs or English learners, but not students who are fluent readers in a language other than English. Students who are fluent readers in their home language are better served by traditional vocabulary instruction or learning experiences intended for English learners.

USING *HIGH NOON VOCABULARY*

High Noon Vocabulary may be used in concert with any other reading instruction program, including *High Noon Reading*. It is meant for small-group or individual instruction guided by a teacher or instructional assistant. In some cases, a capable peer or cross-age tutor may be used for some activities. *High Noon Vocabulary* can also be used with handheld scanners like the Readingpen (readingpen.com).

Within each of the four levels of *High Noon Vocabulary* there are 35 lessons. The sequence of lessons in each level is based on the most common phonics patterns arranged by difficulty. The first lesson in Level A, for example, focuses on words with the short *-a* sound and regular consonant sounds. The last instructional lesson in Level A focuses on the *sh* digraph. Every fifth lesson is a progress monitoring review that allows the teacher to measure how well students have learned the words in the previous four lessons. This lesson also contains an activity page that other students can use independently while the teacher is conducting an individual assessment.

Because the lessons in *High Noon Vocabulary* are based on common sound/spelling patterns, students will develop the ability to decode the lesson words automatically. The practice activities will help students recall the meanings of the words featured in the lesson and learn to derive the meanings of unfamiliar words from context, use structural analysis, and apply other strategies.

Small Group Learning and Oral Interaction

Unlike some vocabulary programs, *High Noon Vocabulary* does not emphasize expressive use of learned vocabulary words through independent writing. Although this is an important skill, it is secondary to the goal of having students read words with understanding. *High Noon Vocabulary* is appropriate for struggling readers, so the focus of the program is on helping them develop proficiency in decoding words, recalling their meaning, and deriving the meaning of unfamiliar words in context. The activities in *High Noon Vocabulary* are "context rich," which means students are provided ample clues to help them crystallize their knowledge of the words they are learning.

The activities in *High Noon Vocabulary* are meant for use with individual students or small groups of students who are reading well below grade level. It is not designed for whole class instruction with students whose reading ability spans the typical range. Even though many of the words are challenging, there are more appropriate materials for whole class instruction.

Because of the high degree of oral interaction that is the basis of *High Noon Vocabulary*, a teacher or other adult should conduct the pretest, discuss the words that are featured in each lesson, and complete the first activity. After that, the interaction of a teacher or adult is recommended, although a peer or cross-age tutor can conduct some of the activities.

The oral interaction that is fundamental to *High Noon Vocabulary* contributes in several ways to the development of students' reading ability. Because so many of the activities involve following along while the teacher or other adult reads, it is likely that students' listening skills will improve. Their decoding ability will improve because of the organization of the books by phonetic clusters, and students will build associations between the words that are in their listening vocabulary with the printed representations. Reading along will promote fluency, and students' comprehension will improve because they will be expected to apply their knowledge of words in novel situations.

Other than the pretest, posttest, and progress monitoring assessments, the activities may be completed by students working alone or with other students. The activities are intended to help students recognize and understand the words, so interaction can contribute to students' success. Keep in mind that the activities are not assessments; rather, they are forms of practice that help students crystallize their knowledge of the target words. The activities should not be graded, but instead should be reviewed with the students after they have completed them.

There is no placement test for *High Noon Vocabulary*. Students for whom the program is appropriate should begin with Lesson 1 and continue through each subsequent lesson. Each level of *High Noon Vocabulary* features sound-spelling patterns of increasing difficulty and words that vary in difficulty. By completing all the lessons, students will improve their decoding skills, will learn the meaning of new words or have the meaning of known words reinforced, and will have an opportunity to apply their knowledge of the words to comprehend spoken and written text. Even if students can decode the words in the first lesson, it is unlikely that they will know the meaning of all the words, and they will undoubtedly benefit from the practice activities in the lesson.

Duplicate each activity page for every student who will use the program. Allow the students to work on the pages, check their own work on the pages, and when they make an error, correct the error on the page. The combination of auditory, visual, and kinesthetic behaviors increases the likelihood that students will decode words and recall their meaning automatically.

If possible, have the students keep a folder of their work. The accumulation of completed work is reinforcing for the students and will motivate them to continue putting forth their best efforts. The collection of the students' work will also demonstrate to friends, family members, and other significant adults the progress the students have made.

Many struggling readers will lack confidence in their own ability and may be unwilling to take chances because their responses might be wrong. Do everything possible to encourage students to take risks, guess at answers when they are not sure which one is correct, and recognize that making mistakes is part of the learning process. If students feel that making an effort will be rewarded whether they are right or wrong, they will be more likely to assume responsibility for their own learning.

Instructional Schedule

High Noon Vocabulary contains 35 lessons, approximately one per week of the school year. For every four content lessons, there is a progress monitoring lesson. Ideally, students would start to use the program at the beginning of the school year. If this is not possible, then the students can begin with Lesson 1 at any time during the school year.

Following is a weekly schedule of use. We strongly encourage the completion of only one lesson page per day. Distributing practice over several days increases the likelihood that students will learn to decode the lesson words and recognize their meanings when they encounter them in print.

Monday   Lesson page 1: Administer pretest (Optional)
Tuesday   Lesson page 2: Review word meanings; complete cloze activity
Wednesday   Lesson page 3: Practice word recognition and application
Thursday   Lesson page 4: Practice word recognition and application
Friday   Lesson page 1: Administer posttest (Optional)

Completing a typical *High Noon Vocabulary* lesson takes no more than ten to fifteen minutes. If the pre- and posttests are not administered, only three instructional days per week will be required. No special training or advanced preparation on the part of the teacher is required.

The first page of each lesson is a pretest of word recognition and word meaning that can be administered to individual students or small groups of students. The pretest may also be used as a posttest. Administering the pre- or posttests is optional. The tests take about five minutes to administer, with another few minutes for scoring and recording, depending on the number of students assessed.

The second page of each lesson contains a brief glossary and a cloze-type activity. The glossary serves as the basis for a discussion of the meaning of each word in the lesson. The cloze-type activity allows students to practice their understanding of the words.

The third and fourth lesson pages contain activities that provide additional practice in recognizing words and applying their meanings. The final activity is a brief section called "Did You Know." This section serves as the basis for interaction between the teacher and the students to expand their knowledge of the lesson words. The section covers topics such as multiple meanings, word origins, roots, and other interesting facts about words. The purpose of "Did You Know" is to culminate the lesson with a motivating activity that will help students broaden their understanding of the lesson words and learn techniques for deriving the meaning of words they encounter in everyday reading.

Assigning *High Noon Vocabulary* As Homework

The activity pages in *High Noon Vocabulary* may be assigned as homework if the student has an opportunity to complete the activities with a capable adult reader. Oral interaction and assisted practice are essential to the success of the program. We recommend that you send a note home with the assignment so that the adult knows that working through the activities with the student is not only permitted, but encouraged.

ACTIVITY DESCRIPTIONS AND INSTRUCTIONS

Most of the learning activities in *High Noon Vocabulary* involve an oral read-along. The read-along strategy will promote fluency and capitalize on the students' receptive language skills. The exception is "On Your Own" in progress monitoring.

There are a variety of response options. The most common is writing the lesson words, which reinforces the students' recognition and understanding of the words.

Did You Know is an oral enrichment activity that introduces students to some vocabulary strategies and gives the teacher the opportunity to make vocabulary more interesting and challenging. It is a culminating activity intended to maintain the motivation of both teachers and students.

In Your Own Words is a scaffolding activity that lets students make connections between the lesson words and what they already know. They answer questions about the lesson words based on their own experiences.

Making Sense is a relatively simple activity that builds fluency and lets students practice the concept of "word." Students divide run-on text into meaningful phrases.

Missing Letter promotes word recognition by presenting an incomplete word and a missing letter. Students are expected to write the completed word. It promotes recall of the word's configuration and is less a spelling activity than another way to get students to "own" the words they are learning in the lesson.

On Your Own is a component of the progress monitoring lesson that gives students an opportunity to work independently. The students don't receive immediate feedback, so they don't know if their answers are correct or incorrect. The delayed feedback will not influence their performance on the assessment. The activity involves the recognition of all the words in the lesson, but only sixteen of them are correct answers. The students can complete the activity before or after they engage in the individual assessment with the teacher.

Opposites is probably the most challenging activity in the program because it asks students to choose a lesson word that is the opposite of a definition. This activity appears just seven times because of the level of challenge and because not all lesson words lend themselves to this activity.

Pretest consists of two parts, decoding and word meaning. The distractors for decoding are nonsense words. The distractors for word meaning are real words that are structurally similar to the target word in one way or another. The distractors are not similar in meaning to the target word. The pretest can be readministered as a posttest. Both the pre- and posttests are optional.

Which One is a simple activity in which students choose which of two words matches a clue. It's a great way for students to learn how to differentiate the meaning of two words they have recently learned.

Word by Word comprises two activities. The first is a review of the lesson words and their meanings. The teacher will be encouraged to elaborate on the meanings as is appropriate for the students. The second part is a cloze-type activity that helps students learn to use context to derive word meaning. It also provides a success-oriented task that follows immediately upon the first review of the words and their meanings.

Word Cross is a puzzle that will help the students recognize the lesson words. It will also give students a chance to review the meanings of the lesson words.

Word Maze is a puzzle in which students add one or more letters to each word in a designated place in the word. It helps students recognize words in a complex background and reinforces their understanding of critical letters.

Word Quest involves questions that the students answer using words from the lesson. The questions are restatements of the definitions of the words.

Word Swap involves exchanging a lesson word with a word or phrase used in a sentence. It's a great way to practice synonym and near-synonym recognition as well as use context to derive word meaning.

Fix the Word presents the definitions of the lesson words and a mismatched list of the words that are scrambled. The student draws a line between the definition and the scrambled word and then writes the word correctly.

Word Find is a puzzle in which students use a pool of letters to write words from the lesson. To complete the task, the students must refer to the lesson words, confirm that the letters are in the list provided, and write the word, then cross it off a list. Completing the activity requires that the student read each lesson word several times.

Word Scramble is a vocabulary-in-context activity in which students read a sentence with a scrambled word. The context of the activity provides clues to the meaning of the word, which is then written correctly beside the sentence.

INSTRUCTIONAL GUIDELINES

Pretest and Posttest

Duplicate the Pretest for each student to be assessed. The Pretest is the first page of each lesson. It is not identified as a pretest in order to avoid raising students' anxieties. The sound/spelling on which the lesson is based is shown on the bottom of the page in order to avoid giving the students clues about the correct answers.

Have the students sit in a quiet, comfortable place. If you are working in a regular classroom, a table or desks in a corner of the room will work well. Distribute the duplicated page to each student. Be sure each student has a pencil or pen. Have the students write their name at the top of the page. Ask them to fold the page approximately in half just above the second set of directions. Folding the page will make it less likely that students will use the answers in the decoding assessment to answer the word meaning assessment.

Introduce the students to the word recognition assessment by paraphrasing the directions below:

We're going to learn some new vocabulary words and practice using them. Before we begin, let's see how much you already know about these words. This activity has two parts. For the first part, listen to each word I say. Draw a circle around the word. If you aren't sure which word is correct, just leave it blank.

Look at Number 1. *Lad*...draw a circle around the word *lad.* (pause for a moment)

Move down to Number 2. (continue for items 1 through 10)

To identify the target words in each lesson, refer to the answer key in the back of this book. Another option is simply to note the words in the assessment that are *not* nonsense words and mark these words on a page you can keep for this purpose.

At the completion of the word recognition assessment, allow the students a moment to rest. Then ask them to turn over the sheet and continue with the word meaning assessment.

Introduce the students to the word meaning assessment by paraphrasing the directions below:

This is the second part of the activity. Look at the word or words in the box. Read them to yourself while I read them out loud. Draw a circle around the answer that means about the same as the word or words in the box. If you aren't sure which answer is correct, take your best guess.

Look at Number 1. *little bit*...which answer means about the same as *little bit?* (pause for a moment)

Move down to Number 2. (continue for items 1 through 10)

At the conclusion of the assessment, collect the students' work. Praise them for their effort, and encourage them by mentioning that you will be reviewing and using the words as part of the next activity. Correct the students' papers and record the number right on the Student Record Form on page 152.

Word by Word

Duplicate the second lesson page, Word by Word, for each student. Distribute the duplicated page to each student. Be sure the students write their names and the date at the top of the page.

Review the lesson words and their meanings with the students. Ask volunteers to read each lesson word aloud after you have read it. Allow students who are confident to attempt the words independently, but be prepared to provide the correct pronunciation if they falter.

Read the definition of each word aloud while the students read along with you. Elaborate on the definition as appropriate for the students. The definitions are brief and are written using simple language in order to allow students to follow along easily. While elaborating, repeat the target word several times, provide examples that the students can understand, and engage them in conversation about the words. The oral interaction about the words is critical to students' internalizing their meanings in a personal way.

Many of the words in *High Noon Vocabulary* have more than one meaning. We have avoided presenting multiple meanings in order to help students grasp at least one meaning of each featured word. The multiple meanings of some words are discussed in the Did You Know section. If students demonstrate sufficient understanding of the featured meaning of the lesson words, they may be introduced to other meanings at the conclusion of the lesson.

After reviewing the meanings of the lesson words, complete the cloze activity with the students. Introduce the students to the activity by explaining that you are going to give them an opportunity to use the words in a sentence. Tell the students that they can refer to the words and their meanings to complete the sentences.

Read the directions aloud to the students. As you read each sentence, say the word "blank" when one appears in the sentence. Read the sentence clearly. Provide help as necessary for the students to find the right answer. You might, for example, paraphrase the text, ask a question that clarifies the meaning of the text, and encourage the students to look at the glossary. Remind the students to say their answers out loud before writing them. Clarify correct answers and point out why incorrect guesses are wrong. Be sure students understand which answer is correct, then give them an opportunity to write the answer in the blank.

Keep in mind that this activity as well as the others is not an assessment. They are practice activities that will be most beneficial if students are encouraged to explore possible answers and then decide on the one they think is correct. The oral engagement, review of possible answers, and process by which students choose the correct answer are important steps in learning to decode the words and understand their meanings.

At the conclusion of the activity, praise the students for their effort and mention that they will have other opportunities to practice using the words. Allow them to use the lesson words and definitions in other activities. Encourage the students to collect their work in a folder. Have them organize the folder with the earliest work first. On a periodic basis, review the students' folders to promote a sense of accomplishment about the words they have learned.

Other Activities

Lesson pages three and four should each be completed on separate days. The activities on these pages vary from lesson to lesson. Each activity has a set of directions, and in some cases, a sample has been completed for the students.

Read the directions out loud to the students. If there are elements of an activity that the students can complete independently, allow them to do so. If they need help, provide it as necessary. Whenever the directions involve reading with the students, be sure to do so or ask an accomplished student to do so. Interact with the students as necessary, and encourage both paired and small group learning. In addition to promoting vocabulary development, this interaction will also promote fluency as students read along while hearing text read with appropriate prosody.

The Did You Know activity is found on page four of some lessons. This activity is a teacher-directed review of interesting facts about some of the words in the lesson. It is the basis for a discussion with the students about information such as multiple meanings of words, alternate forms of words, synonyms, roots and affixes, historic facts about words, mnemonic strategies, and using context to derive meaning.

PROGRESS MONITORING

The progress monitoring assessments are critical to students' success. They provide information that can inform instruction and allow you to make the adjustments needed to improve student learning. Unlike the pre- and posttests, the progress monitoring assessment is individually administered.

In addition to pages from *High Noon Vocabulary*, you will need a pencil and a stopwatch or a watch with a second hand. Both the word reading and word meaning assessments are timed.

Duplicate the first three pages of the progress monitoring lesson for each student. The fourth page is an optional activity page that other students can use independently while you are engaged in assessment. Duplicate the fourth page if you want students to complete it. Students may also engage in free reading or any other activity you feel is appropriate.

Word Reading

Word Reading is the first page of the progress monitoring lesson. It is not identified as a test in order to avoid raising student's anxieties. The second page is used to record students' responses, and the third page is for the word meaning assessment.

Have the students sit in a quiet, comfortable place. If you are working in a regular classroom, a table or desks in a corner of the room will work well. Distribute the duplicated page to each student. Be sure each student has a pencil or pen. Have the students write their names and the date at the top of the page. Introduce the students to the word recognition assessment by paraphrasing the directions below. The directions also appear on the word reading record form.

Read each word out loud. Start with the top row and read from left to right.
(If necessary, remind the students how to read from left to right and from top to bottom.)
Try to read quickly and correctly. If you aren't sure how to read a word, take your best guess. You may skip a word, but only if you can't read it at all. Just say "skip." Are you ready? You may begin.

Begin timing when the student starts reading. Stop the assessment after one minute or if the student makes four errors in a row. As an option, you may have the student read all the words.

(Some students who have mastered the words may be able to read all of them in less than a minute. When this occurs, simply record the total number of words read correctly. We advise against using the time it takes the students to read all the words as a measure of their progress. Little useful information is gained about students' decoding abilities by following this practice, and students may attempt to read too quickly and make more mistakes than they would while reading at an optimal pace.)

At the completion of the word recognition assessment, allow the students a moment to rest. Then continue with the word meaning assessment. You will need page 3 of the progress monitoring lesson to record the results of the assessment.

Introduce the students to the word meaning assessment by paraphrasing the directions below. The directions also appear on the word meaning record form.

Listen to each word I say. In your own words, tell me what the word means or use it in a sentence. If you aren't sure what a word means, take your best guess. You may skip a word, but only if you don't have any idea what it means. Just say "skip." Are you ready? Let's begin.

Read each word out loud. Start with the top row and read from left to right. Begin timing when you say the first word. Stop the assessment after one minute or if the student makes four errors in a row.

A student may answer correctly in several ways:

- saying a synonym for the target word
- explaining the meaning of the target word
- using the target word in a sentence
- providing an example that demonstrates understanding of the target word

Once a student has answered correctly, move on to the next word. If a student demonstrates knowledge of a word but continues to elaborate, interrupt by saying "That's correct. Here's the next word." Allowing the student to elaborate beyond the basic definition diminishes the time the student has to attempt other words.

Record the results of the assessment on the student record sheet (page 3 of the progress monitoring lesson). Put a check mark beside each word the student defines correctly. Draw a line through each word the student defines incorrectly or skips. Circle the last word the student attempts within one minute. Record the correct number of words per minute in the space at the bottom of each page, on the Student Record form on page 152, and on the Progress Monitoring graph on page 151.

(After the student has completed the one-minute assessment, you may choose to allow the student to define all the words. Consider this supplemental assessment only if the student is comfortable defining the words and demonstrates knowledge of most of them. Allowing a student to attempt all of the words is a power assessment rather than a speed assessment and provides another source of information that can guide instruction. Some students who have not yet achieved automaticity in their knowledge of the meanings of the words may be able to recall their meanings if given enough time.)

On Your Own

The fourth page of the progress monitoring lesson is an activity that students can complete independently while you are assessing other students. Students should be able to complete the activity by themselves or with the assistance of a partner.

The activity asks students to find a word from one of the lessons that means about the same as a synonym or brief phrase. There are 16 items, but students have to consider all 40 words from the previous four lessons to find the answers. The activity engages students while other students are being assessed and gives students an opportunity to apply the vocabulary skills they have recently acquired. Because the students have no feedback about their performance, the activity should have little effect on the assessment.

Note: A discussion of progress monitoring can be found on page 150.

Name_____

Listen to each word I say. Draw a circle around the word.

1.	lob	tob	lof
2.	kull	lell	lull
3.	doch	dock	dosk
4.	vod	nid	nod
5.	moss	monn	woss
6.	pog	fog	foj
7.	odd	opp	uld
8.	bick	bulg	buck
9.	lud	bud	gud
10.	kug	puj	pug

Look at the word or words in the box. Listen as I read them. Draw a circle around the answer that means about the same as the word or words in the box.

1.	mist	mud	fog	pot
2.	tiny plant	sink	rest	moss
3.	speak softly	clip	lull	dive
4.	kind of dog	pug	hay	job
5.	part of a plant	low	owl	bud
6.	strange	yet	odd	ago
7.	move your head	nod	set	tag
8.	place for ships	kite	dock	bank
9.	throw high	win	fan	lob
10.	kick and jump	buck	gate	mill

LESSON 2

Word by Word

buck	to jump up and down	**moss**	a tiny plant that grows in the shade
bud	part of a plant		
dock	where boats are unloaded	**nod**	to move your head up and down
fog	a cloud near the ground		
lob	to throw something high	**odd**	strange
lull	to make a person calm	**pug**	a kind of small dog

Read each sentence to yourself as I read it out loud. Choose a word from the list above that fits best in each sentence. Only one word will fit best in each sentence. Write the word in the blank.

1. That horse is not tame and will _____ to get the rider off.

2. The tree might be dead. It does not have a single _____ on it.

3. Juan gave a _____ to show he wanted to go with us.

4. There are many boats at the _____.

5. The driver could not see well because of the _____.

6. Penny gives her _____ a treat every morning.

7. There is _____ growing all over that log.

8. Grandmother tried to _____ the baby to sleep.

9. Joe will _____ the ball into the air.

10. Beth found a strange rock with an _____ color.

Name _____

Read each definition on the list. Think of the word from the lesson that matches the definition. Find each word in the grid. Draw a circle around the word and cross off the definition on the list. The words can go in any direction. One has been done for you.

- ~~to jump up and down~~
- part of a plant
- a place where boats arrive
- misty weather
- to throw something into the air
- to calm a person or an animal
- a plant that likes the shade
- to shake your head
- strange or unusual
- a small dog with a funny face

l	m	o	s	s	k
u	b	d	o	c	k
l	n	b	u	d	f
l	o	b	c	d	o
o	d	d	p	u	g

Read each group of letters. Put a slash between the letters so the phrase makes sense. A word from the lesson is in each phrase. One has been done for you.

run/and/buck

softgreenmoss

lullthehorse

lobaball

afriendlypug

thethickfog

atinybud

awoodendock

anoddsound

nodherhead

LESSON 2

Word Swap

Read each sentence to yourself as I read it out loud. Look at the underlined part in each sentence. Choose a word from the box below that can replace the underlined part. Write the word in the blank. One has been done for you.

buck	~~bud~~	dock	fog	lob	lull	moss	nod	odd	pug

1. The <u>green oval</u> on the stem will turn into a flower. _____**bud**_____

2. A <u>heavy mist</u> covered the city's streets. _____

3. During a storm, Sheri will <u>speak softly to</u> the dog. _____

4. The <u>unusual</u> rock was yellow and red. _____

5. In the shade of the tree grew some <u>tiny green plants</u>. _____

6. A young horse will <u>jump up and down</u> when it is excited. _____

7. My friend has a <u>small dog</u> with a curly tail. _____

8. Luke can <u>throw</u> the ball over the house. _____

9. Gina began to <u>shake her head</u> to show she understood. _____

10. The ship's workers unloaded boxes onto the <u>wooden platform</u>.

_____

Did You Know?

The **pug** is a small dog, but it is strong and brave. Chinese emperors have had these dogs for thousands of years.

The artichoke is a vegetable that people eat. It is the **bud** of a plant.

Horses used in rodeos are trained to **buck** hard to throw their riders.

Name_____

Listen to each word I say. Draw a circle around the word.

1.	zool	xeal	zeal
2.	chake	quake	plake
3.	pune	gane	pane
4.	heal	heak	feal
5.	xain	vain	voon
6.	jeer	feer	jeec
7.	leen	keen	kees
8.	veek	mouk	meek
9.	heed	keed	heep
10.	gaje	gape	gope

Word Meaning

Look at the word or words in the box. Listen as I read them. Draw a circle around the answer that means about the same as the word or words in the box.

1.	listen to	heed	late	dish
2.	shake	catch	prize	quake
3.	quiet	meek	read	gate
4.	too proud	cage	vain	tail
5.	stare	hole	gape	feed
6.	sharp	deep	aunt	keen
7.	piece of glass	nail	pane	seat
8.	shout bad things	jeer	game	near
9.	make better	keep	barn	heal
10.	liking a lot	hold	zeal	face

LESSON 3

Word by Word

gape	to stare at	**meek**	quiet and not proud
heal	to fix an injury or illness	**pane**	the glass in a window
heed	to pay attention to	**quake**	to shake
jeer	to shout bad things	**vain**	too proud
keen	sharp	**zeal**	liking something very much

Read each sentence to yourself as I read it out loud. Choose a word from the list above that fits best in each sentence. Only one word will fit best in each sentence. Write the word in the blank.

1. Mona broke her arm last year. It took a while to _____.

2. The coach asked the fans not to _____ at the other team.

3. Visitors to the zoo usually _____ at the unusual animals.

4. A _____ person will not usually say too much.

5. The _____ of glass is thick to keep the cold air out.

6. Jeff has great _____ for all sports.

7. Shaina cut the bread into thin slices with the _____ knife.

8. The ground began to _____ when the big truck went by.

9. Be sure to _____ all the directions when you fix the computer.

10. No one likes people who are _____ about the way they look.

Name_____

Look at each word in the first column. It is missing one letter. The missing letter is in the second column. Decide where the missing letter fits and write the correct word in the blank. One has been done for you.

Word	Missing Letter	
1. van	i	__vain__
2. ken	e	_____
3. hal	e	_____
4. pae	n	_____
5. eal	z	_____
6. gae	p	_____
7. mek	e	_____
8. eer	j	_____
9. quae	k	_____
10. hed	e	_____

Opposites

Read each definition below as I read it out loud. Find the word in the box that means the opposite of the definition. Write the word in the blank beside the definition. One has been done for you.

~~gape~~ heal heed jeer keen meek pane quake vain zeal

Definition	Opposite
1. To look away from	~~gape~~
2. Dull	_____
3. Loud and pushy	_____
4. Not liking something at all	_____
5. To get sick	_____

Name_____

Read each question to yourself while I read it out loud. Think of the word from the lesson that best answers the question. Write the word on the line after the question. The words from the lesson are in the box.

gape   heal   heed   jeer   keen   meek   pane   quake   vain   zeal

1. What is it called when you pay attention to something?

   _____

2. How do you describe something sharp? _____

3. What is it called when you get better after being hurt?

   _____

4. What is a piece of glass in a window called? _____

5. What is a person called who is not loud or proud? _____

6. If you like something very much, what is it called?_____

7. What is it called when you stare at something? _____

8. When something shakes, what is it called? _____

9. When you shout bad things, what is it called? _____

10. How would you describe a person who is too proud? _____

Did You Know?

Keen means **sharp** in different ways. A **sharp** knife is **keen**. A smart person has a **keen** mind. Long ago, kids used **keen** and **sharp** as slang words to mean something was great.

If someone has a lot of **zeal**, they are said to be **zealous**. **Zealous** is pronounced a lot like **jealous**.

You can remember what **heal** means because it is the first part of **healthy**. When you **heal**, you get **healthy**.

vain	pane	lime	zeal
jute	dock	dill	heal
due	rill	meek	pug
lob	pose	peck	lull
quite	quake	cope	fog
fine	keen	mule	bid
code	pal	jeer	fad
wit	odd	moss	bud
ban	sap	buck	sole
deck	nod	heed	gape

Word Reading Directions: Read each word out loud. Start with the top row and read from left to right. Try to read quickly and correctly. If you aren't sure how to read a word, take your best guess. You may skip a word, but only if you can't read it at all. Just say "skip." Are you ready? You may begin.

Administration and Scoring Directions: Begin timing when the student starts reading. Stop after one minute or if the student makes four errors in a row.

Put a check mark beside each word the student reads correctly. Draw a line through each word the student reads incorrectly or skips. Circle the last word the student reads within one minute. Record the correct number of words per minute in the space at the bottom of the page and on the Progress Monitoring Form on page 151.

Name_____   Date_____

vain	pane	lime	zeal
jute	dock	dill	heal
due	rill	meek	pug
lob	pose	peck	lull
quite	quake	cope	fog
fine	keen	mule	bid
code	pal	jeer	fad
wit	odd	moss	bud
ban	sap	buck	sole
deck	nod	heed	gape

Word Meaning Directions: Listen to each word I say. In your own words, tell me what the word means. If you aren't sure what a word means, take your best guess. You may skip a word, but only if you don't have any idea what it means. Just say "skip." Are you ready? Let's begin.

Administration and Scoring Directions: Read each word out loud. Start with the top row and read from left to right. Begin timing when you say the first word. Stop after one minute or if the student makes four errors in a row.

Put a check mark beside each word the student defines correctly. Draw a line through each word the student defines incorrectly or skips. Circle the last word the student attempts within one minute. Record the correct number of words per minute in the space at the bottom of the page and on the Progress Monitoring Form on page 151.

Name_____ Date_____

nod	meek	moss	quite
lime	sap	gape	dill
fog	keen	pose	rill
mule	code	pal	cope
lob	zeal	wit	bud
lull	heed	jute	deck
pane	fine	pug	jeer
sole	vain	heal	ban
peck	quake	bid	fad
due	odd	dock	buck

On Your Own

Name_____

Read each word below. Choose a word from the box that means about the same as the word. Write the word in the blank. One has been done for you. The words from the lessons are at the bottom of the page. You will not use all the words.

friend   **pal**   shake _____

male deer _____   mist _____

too proud _____   forbid _____

make better _____   sharp _____

kind of dog _____   strange _____

plant part _____   throw _____

small stream_____   stare _____

piece of glass _____   listen to _____

ban	bid	buck	bud	code
cope	deck	dill	dock	due
fad	fine	fog	gape	heal
heed	jeer	jute	keen	lime
lob	lull	meek	moss	mule
nod	odd	~~pal~~	pane	peck
pose	pug	quake	quite	rill
sap	sole	vain	wit	zeal

Name_____

Look at the letters below. You can make at least six words from the lesson using the letters. You can use a letter more than once. Write each word you find on a line. Cross off the word from the list after you write it. One has been done for you.

a b c d f g i k l n o p r s

| brink ~~cling~~ dank flank link pang plank prank prong slang |

_____ **cling** _____   _____

_____   _____

_____   _____

_____

In Your Own Words

Directions: Read each question to yourself while I read it out loud. Write your answer on the line after each question.

1. What might be **dank**? _____

_____

2. Who do you know who likes to play a **prank**? _____

_____

3. What saying is an example of **slang**? _____

_____

4. What has a **prong**? _____

_____

5. Where would you buy a **plank**? _____

_____

Name _____

LESSON 6

Word Scramble

Read each sentence to yourself. The underlined word has scrambled letters. Think about the word you can make from the letters. Write the word in the blank beside the sentence. One has been done for you.

1. Kids use different <u>angls</u> than their parents. _____**slang**_____

2. The <u>pnorg</u> of the fork was bent. _____

3. Each <u>knil</u> of the chain was made of steel. _____

4. Jan hurt his leg playing a <u>rankp</u> on his brother. _____

5. A <u>pagn</u> in her leg caused Beth to limp. _____

6. The team was on the <u>knrbi</u> of winning the game. _____

7. Juan used a saw to cut the <u>lnapk</u>. _____

8. The baby wants to <u>nglci</u> to its mother. _____

9. The horse's <u>flnak</u> was dirty from rolling on the ground. _____

10. The cave was beautiful but <u>nkad</u>. _____

Did You Know?

Slang changes from place to place, even in the same country. **Slang** also changes over time. Some old **slang** words like *swell* or *nifty* aren't used any more.

The word **flank** is often used to describe the side of an animal. It may also be used to tell about the side of an army.

A **prank** is usually a foolish joke played on a person.

LESSON

7

Word Wise

Listen to each word I say. Draw a circle around the word.

1.	hutch	lutch	hunth
2.	flatch	tharch	thatch
3.	plutch	clutch	clatch
4.	tatch	futch	latch
5.	botch	potch	bonch
6.	chetch	sketch	skerth
7.	slatch	snutch	snatch
8.	fench	fetch	hetch
9.	notch	nutch	cutch
10.	barch	datch	batch

Word Meaning

Look at the word or words in the box. Listen as I read them. Draw a circle around the answer that means about the same as the word or words in the box.

1.	do wrong	catch	botch	boast
2.	get	match	fence	fetch
3.	a cut	north	notch	pitch
4.	kind of lock	lunch	bench	latch
5.	bunch	batch	march	watch
6.	grab	sniff	snatch	branch
7.	cupboard	hutch	patch	hunch
8.	draw	skate	stretch	sketch
9.	hold tight	clutch	splash	cluck
10.	straw	scratch	thatch	thread

Name_____

LESSON 7

Word by Word

batch	an amount or group	**latch**	holds a door closed
botch	to do something badly	**notch**	a small cut
clutch	to hold tightly	**sketch**	to draw quickly
fetch	to bring something back	**snatch**	to grab
hutch	a cupboard with shelves and drawers	**thatch**	straw used for a roof

Read each sentence to yourself as I read it out loud. Choose a word from the list above that fits best in each sentence. Only one word will fit best in each sentence. Write the word in the blank.

1. Jenna asked her mom to make a _____ of cookies.

2. We helped out after dinner. We put the dishes back in the _____.

3. He can _____ a cartoon in ten minutes.

4. Long ago in Europe, a house might have a roof made of _____.

5. Sam studied hard so he would not _____ the test.

6. The dog got out because the _____ on the gate was broken.

7. Pedro had to _____ the umbrella so it wouldn't blow away.

8. The carpenter cut a _____ on the edge of the piece of wood.

9. Mother asked me to _____ some milk from the refrigerator.

10. Miguel was able to _____ the ball out of the air with his bare hands.

Read each definition on the list. Think of the word from the lesson that matches the definition. Find each word in the grid. Draw a circle around the word and cross off the definition on the list. The words can go in any direction. One has been done for you.

- ~~a bunch of something, like cookies~~
- to mess something up
- to hold tight
- to go and get something
- a cupboard
- a kind of a lock
- a little cut or nick
- to draw quickly
- to grab something quickly
- straw used to make a roof

s	k	e	t	c	h	i	c	i
n	o	t	c	h	h	b	l	b
a	r	q	c	c	a	a	u	o
t	n	t	t	u	f	t	t	t
c	u	a	x	y	n	c	c	c
h	l	f	e	t	c	h	h	h

Read each group of letters. Put a slash between the letters so the phrase makes sense. A word from the lesson is in each phrase. One has been done for you.

made/a/sketch

aprettyhutch

botchthejob

cutanotch

fetchastick

clutchthebag

closethelatch

fixthethatch

batchofcookies

snatchanapple

LESSON 7

Word Swap

Read each sentence to yourself as I read it out loud. Look at the underlined part in each sentence. Choose a word from the box that can replace the underlined part. Write the word in the blank. One has been done for you.

batch	~~botch~~	clutch	fetch	hutch
latch	notch	sketch	snatch	thatch

1. Andy managed to <u>mess up</u> the job he was doing. **botch**

2. Liza made a <u>quick drawing</u> of the tree in her yard. _____

3. My dog likes to <u>chase and bring back</u> sticks. _____

4. The roof of the old barn was made of <u>straw</u>. _____

5. The <u>lock</u> on the gate doesn't use a key. _____

6. Mom cooked a <u>bunch</u> of cookies for us. _____

7. Dex tried to <u>grab</u> the apple from the tree. _____

8. Fran made a <u>small cut</u> in the piece of wood. _____

9. The dishes are in the <u>cupboard</u> in the dining room. _____

10. Be sure to <u>hold</u> the package tightly. _____

Listen to each word I say. Draw a circle around the word.

1.	glead	fread	knead
2.	wrath	crath	wreth
3.	ching	wrint	wring
4.	slent	scent	chent
5.	gnat	gnal	snat
6.	gru	gnu	gne
7.	cnit	knip	knit
8.	cren	wren	tren
9.	knack	knath	bnack
10.	stene	scune	scene

Look at the word or words in the box. Listen as I read them. Draw a circle around the answer that means about the same as the word or words in the box.

1.	skill	knock	knack	snack
2.	wild ox	snug	luck	gnu
3.	kind of bird	wren	wrap	then
4.	part of a play	even	scene	shine
5.	make cloth	knit	hint	pink
6.	twist	bring	wrist	wring
7.	anger	wrath	breath	strap
8.	small fly	hang	gnat	snap
9.	smell	pinch	spent	scent
10.	squeeze	ready	knead	break

Name_____

gnat	a small fly	**scene**	part of a play
gnu	an African animal like an ox	**scent**	a nice smell
		wrath	anger
knack	a smart way to do something	**wren**	a small bird
		wring	to remove water by twisting
knead	to press and squeeze		
knit	to make cloth by looping yarn		

Read each sentence to yourself as I read it out loud. Choose a word from the list above that fits best in each sentence. Only one word will fit best in each sentence. Write the word in the blank.

1. My mother is teaching me to _____ a scarf.

2. The king's _____ was caused by thieves stealing from poor people.

3. Sue has a _____ for doing her math problems.

4. The _____ built a nest on our porch.

5. To see a _____, you have to go to Africa or a zoo.

6. Wally practiced for his _____ in the play.

7. Dad showed Nick how to _____ the bread dough.

8. The tiny bug that was bothering us was a _____.

9. A skunk's _____ does not smell very good.

10. After the storm, Carlos had to _____ the water from his hat.

LESSON 8

Missing Letter

Look at each word in the first column. It is missing one letter. The missing letter is in the second column. Decide where the missing letter fits and write the correct word in the blank. One has been done for you.

	Word	Missing Letter	
1.	scnt	e	**scent**
2.	wath	r	_____
3.	kack	n	_____
4.	cene	s	_____
5.	nead	k	_____
6.	gu	n	_____
7.	ren	w	_____
8.	wing	r	_____
9.	gnt	a	_____
10.	kit	n	_____

Read each definition below as I read it out loud. Find the word in the box that means the opposite of the definition. Write the word in the blank beside the definition. One has been done for you.

Opposites

gnat gnu ~~knack~~ knead knit scene scent wrath wren wring

Definition	Opposite
1. A foolish way to do something	**knack**
2. Calmness	_____
3. To make something wet	_____
4. To hammer something hard	_____
5. No smell at all	_____

Name _____

LESSON 8

Word Quest

Read each question to yourself while I read it out loud. Think of the word from the lesson that best answers the question. Write the word on the line after the question. The words from the lesson are in the box.

| gnat gnu knack knead knit scene scent wrath wren wring |

1. When you squeeze dough, what is it called? _____

2. What is an African animal like an ox? _____

3. What is a nice smell called? _____

4. What is it called when you make cloth with yarn? _____

5. What is a small bird? _____

6. What is a small fly? _____

7. If you are angry, what do you feel? _____

8. What is it called if you do something the smart way? _____

9. What is it called when you remove water by twisting? _____

10. What is part of a play called? _____

Did You Know?

A **scent** is a good smell, like a flower. It is different from an odor, which is a smell that is not nice. The smell of a skunk is an odor.

At a zoo, the **gnu** is a popular animal. People want to see the animal with such an unusual name.

Another name for a **gnat** that bites people is the no-see-um. Can you guess how it got this name?

Name _____

Listen to each word I say. Draw a circle around the word.

1.	hedge	henge	hudge
2.	rodge	nidge	ridge
3.	fodge	lodge	longe
4.	predge	pledge	plende
5.	budge	bulde	hurge
6.	stedge	sledge	slenge
7.	ludge	tedge	ledge
8.	codge	dodge	didge
9.	gludge	gruthe	grudge
10.	trudge	crudge	tradge

Look at the word or words in the box. Listen as I read them. Draw a circle around the answer that means about the same as the word or words in the box.

1.	avoid	found	dodge	finger
2.	kind of hill	spend	around	ridge
3.	row of bushes	string	hedge	change
4.	large sled	strange	spring	sledge
5.	move	budge	behind	begin
6.	bad feeling	grudge	trunk	charge
7.	cabin	along	lodge	grade
8.	walk	struck	belong	trudge
9.	rock shelf	ledge	danger	lend
10.	promise	please	splash	pledge

Name_____

budge	to move	**pledge**	to promise
dodge	to get out of the way	**ridge**	a hill with a long, thin top
grudge	a bad feeling		
hedge	a row of bushes growing together	**sledge**	a large sled
		trudge	to walk with a heavy step
ledge	a narrow shelf of rock		
lodge	a kind of big cabin		

Read each sentence to yourself as I read it out loud. Choose a word from the list above that fits best in each sentence. Only one word will fit best in each sentence. Write the word in the blank.

1. Pedro tried to _____ the ball his sister threw at him.

2. The mountain climbers rested on a narrow _____ just a foot wide.

3. Lucy's neighbor has a _____ of rose bushes.

4. The horses pulled the _____ through the snow.

5. The door would not _____. It was jammed shut.

6. Sue made a _____ to walk her dog every day.

7. The children had to _____ through the deep snow.

8. The family stayed in a small _____ out in the woods.

9. Pete felt a _____ because other kids teased him.

10. Tall trees grew on the _____ at the top of the mountain.

Name _____

Read each question to yourself as I read it out loud. Circle the answer you think is correct. One has been done for you.

1. If you promise, do you **budge** or (**pledge**)?

2. If you walk with heavy steps, do you **trudge** or **dodge**?

3. Is a row of bushes a **sledge** or a **hedge**?

4. Is a big cabin a **lodge** or a **ridge**?

5. Does a mountain climber rest on a **grudge** or a **ledge**?

Look at the Word Maze puzzle below. The letters _d_ and _g_ are missing from each word. Write the letters _d_ and _g_ where they belong to complete each word. One has been done for you.

s	l	e	d	g	e			h
	t	r	u		e		e
b	u			e		r	
	d	o		e		i	
g	r	u		e			e
l	e		e			
l	o		e		e	
	p	l	e		e	

Name _____

Read each definition to yourself as I read it out loud. Find the scrambled word that matches the definition. Draw a line from the definition to the correct scrambled word. Fix the word and write it on the line beside the scrambled word. One has been done for you.

a kind of big cabin   dregug   _____

to walk with heavy steps   eelgdp   _____

to promise   seeldg   _____

a hill with a long, thin top begud   _____

a large sled   ehgde   _____

to move   urtged   _____

a narrow shelf of rock   ddgoe   _____

to get out of the way   dgole   ___**lodge**___

a bad feeling   egeld   _____

row of bushes
growing together   dregi   _____

Pledge is both a verb or a noun, just as the word **promise** is. You make a **promise** or **promise** to do something. You also make a **pledge** or **pledge** to do something.

The word **trudge** describes walking that is very tiring. What makes it tiring is the surface on which you are walking. You would normally **trudge** through heavy snow, mud, or sand. You might also trudge if you were carrying a heavy load.

scene	notch	wring	trudge
thatch	wrath	hutch	ridge
prank	lodge	gnat	fetch
knack	dodge	slang	batch
botch	pledge	clutch	pang
gnu	dank	grudge	knead
sketch	budge	latch	prong
scent	plank	snatch	knit
wren	cling	link	flank
sledge	hedge	ledge	brink

Word Reading Directions: Read each word out loud. Start with the top row and read from left to right. Try to read quickly and correctly. If you aren't sure how to read a word, take your best guess. You may skip a word, but only if you can't read it at all. Just say "skip." Are you ready? You may begin.

Administration and Scoring Directions: Begin timing when the student starts reading. Stop the assessment after one minute or if the student makes four errors in a row.

Put a check mark beside each word the student reads correctly. Draw a line through each word the student reads incorrectly or skips. Circle the last word the student reads within one minute. Record the correct number of words per minute in the space at the bottom of the page and on the Progress Monitoring Form on page 151.

Name_____ Date_____

scene	notch	wring	trudge
thatch	wrath	hutch	ridge
prank	lodge	gnat	fetch
knack	dodge	slang	batch
botch	pledge	clutch	pang
gnu	dank	grudge	knead
sketch	budge	latch	prong
scent	plank	snatch	knit
wren	cling	link	flank
sledge	hedge	ledge	brink

Progress Monitoring

Word Meaning Directions: Listen to each word I say. In your own words, tell me what the word means. If you aren't sure what a word means, take your best guess. You may skip a word, but only if you don't have any idea what it means. Just say "skip." Are you ready? Let's begin.

Administration and Scoring Directions: Read each word out loud. Start with the top row and read from left to right. Begin timing when you say the first word. Stop the assessment after one minute or if the student makes four errors in a row.

Put a check mark beside each word the student defines correctly. Draw a line through each word the student defines incorrectly or skips. Circle the last word the student attempts within one minute. Record the correct number of words per minute in the space at the bottom of the page and on the Progress Monitoring Form on page 151.

Name_____ Date_____

hedge	gnat	snatch	botch
wring	cling	brink	hutch
pang	dank	dodge	lodge
grudge	sketch	budge	clutch
knack	trudge	scent	knit
batch	ledge	thatch	sledge
notch	gnu	fetch	latch
flank	scene	ridge	wren
slang	pledge	knead	prong
prank	plank	wrath	link

Name_____

On Your Own

Read each word below. Choose a word from the box that means about the same as the word. Write the word in the blank. One has been done for you. The words from the lesson are at the bottom of the page. You will not use all the words.

anger	**wrath**	draw	_____
straw	_____	cabin	_____
piece of chain	_____	grab	_____
small cut	_____	damp	_____
promise	_____	edge	_____
small bug	_____	bunch	_____
row of bushes	_____	rock shelf	_____
sharp pain	_____	nice smell	_____

batch	botch	brink	budge	cling
clutch	dank	dodge	fetch	flank
gnat	gnu	grudge	hedge	hutch
knack	knead	knit	latch	ledge
link	lodge	notch	pang	plank
pledge	prank	prong	ridge	scene
scent	sketch	slang	sledge	snatch
thatch	trudge	~~wrath~~	wren	wring

Name_____

Listen to each word I say. Draw a circle around the word.

1.	gnarl	crarl	gnald
2.	starl	snarl	snirl
3.	stark	slark	starp
4.	slard	sherp	shard
5.	tarsh	harsh	hersh
6.	barm	harm	horm
7.	tart	trat	lart
8.	darge	berge	barge
9.	nar	mar	mav
10.	char	thar	chur

Look at the word or words in the box. Listen as I read them. Draw a circle around the answer that means about the same as the word or words in the box.

1.	burn	chair	scar	char
2.	damage	mar	tar	jar
3.	cruel	charge	first	harsh
4.	lump on tree	gnarl	large	pearl
5.	sweet and sour	trap	tart	star
6.	growl	sneak	spark	snarl
7.	bare	sharp	stark	track
8.	boat	bring	branch	barge
9.	piece	hard	shard	shark
10.	hurt	harm	park	farm

LESSON 11

Word by Word

barge	a flat boat used to carry things
char	to burn
gnarl	a hard lump or knot on a tree
harm	to hurt
harsh	cruel or unkind
mar	to spoil or damage something
shard	a sharp piece of something
snarl	to growl
stark	plain and bare
tart	a good flavor that is a little sour

Read each sentence to yourself as I read it out loud. Choose a word from the list above that fits best in each sentence. Only one word will fit best in each sentence. Write the word in the blank.

1. Be careful not to _____ the top of the table.

2. The loud noise made the dog _____.

3. Karen dropped the bottle. A _____ of glass cut her foot.

4. The pie tasted sweet but was a little _____.

5. The oak tree had a _____ on its trunk as big as a bowling ball.

6. The _____ carried wheat down the Mississippi River.

7. After the movers took the furniture, the empty house looked _____.

8. Don't feed candy to zoo animals. It will _____ them.

9. Judy was sorry for the _____ words she said to her friend.

10. Ken was careful not to _____ the vegetables on the grill.

Name _____

Look at the letters below. You can make at least six words from the lesson using the letters. You can use a letter more than once. Write each word you find on a line. Cross off the word from the list after you write it. One has been done for you.

a b c e g h k l m n r s t

| barge | char | gnarl | harm | harsh | ~~mar~~ | shard | snarl | stark | tart |

_____ **mar** _____   _____

_____   _____

_____   _____

_____   _____

Read each question to yourself while I read it out loud. Write your answer on the line after each question.

1. What animal might **snarl**? _____

_____

2. Where would you see a **barge**? _____

_____

3. What might taste **tart**? _____

_____

4. How would you **char** something? _____

_____

5. What might **mar** the top of a table? _____

_____

Name_____

Read each sentence to yourself. The underlined word has scrambled letters. Think about the word you can make from the letters. Write the word in the blank beside the sentence. One has been done for you.

1. The grapes were too <u>trat</u> for me. _____**tart**_____

2. Saying <u>sharh</u> things is never nice. _____

3. Be careful not to <u>rach</u> the food on the grill. _____

4. If you slide a chair, you might <u>amr</u> the floor. _____

5. Ben moved the bush but did not <u>mahr</u> it. _____

6. The desert was <u>krsta</u> and rocky. _____

7. Leah found a <u>sdhar</u> from an old pot. _____

8. A squirrel sat on a <u>glanr</u> on the tree. _____

9. If you bother a dog, it might <u>slarn</u>. _____

10. A huge <u>bgear</u> floated down the river. _____

Did You Know?

A **gnarled** tree has many lumps, knots, or twisted branches.

Scientists like to find **shards** of old pots. The **shards** can help them learn about people who lived long ago.

Name _____

LESSON 12

Word Wise

Listen to each word I say. Draw a circle around the word.

1.	garge	gorge	gorfe
2.	mord	cord	comd
3.	storch	scarch	scorch
4.	scorn	slorn	scorv
5.	dort	port	porf
6.	lorge	ferge	forge
7.	force	korce	ferce
8.	slork	stort	stork
9.	ferd	pord	ford
10.	form	folm	fomt

Word Meaning

Look at the word or words in the box. Listen as I read them. Draw a circle around the answer that means about the same as the word or words in the box.

1.	place for ships	sort	worn	port
2.	valley	gorge	group	north
3.	power	frost	force	horse
4.	shape	fort	front	form
5.	cross a stream	corn	ford	born
6.	furnace	forge	before	floor
7.	water bird	sport	stork	store
8.	dislike	storm	horn	scorn
9.	burn	scorch	scarf	porch
10.	thick string	word	cord	crop

High Noon Vocabulary B: Controlled -r: or **45**

Name _____

LESSON 12

Word by Word

cord	thick string	**port**	a place for ships to dock
force	power		
ford	to walk through a stream	**scorch**	to burn
forge	a furnace used to heat metal	**scorn**	a feeling of dislike
form	appearance or shape	**stork**	a tall bird that likes water

Read each sentence to yourself as I read it out loud. Choose a word from the list above that fits best in each sentence. Only one word will fit best in each sentence. Write the word in the blank.

1. Tim tied the sticks together with a piece of _____.

2. The _____ of the wind almost knocked the trees over.

3. The blacksmith used a _____ to fix the horseshoes.

4. Nina's favorite bird at the pond in the park was the _____.

5. Charles got his shoes and pants wet when he had to _____ the stream.

6. The _____ of the dark clouds made it look like a storm was coming.

7. The sailors docked their ship in the _____.

8. The hikers had a hard time getting through the steep _____.

9. The store's owner felt _____ for people who stole things.

10. Sandra had to put on sun screen or her skin would _____.

Name _____

Read each definition on the list. Think of the word from the lesson that matches the definition. Find each word in the grid. Draw a circle around the word and cross off the definition on the list. The words can go in any direction. One has been done for you.

- ~~thick string or thin rope~~
- a furnace used to heat metal until it melts
- power or strength
- to walk through a stream or river
- what something looks like
- a rocky valley with steep sides
- a place where ships come in
- to burn
- when you look down on someone
- a tall water bird with a long bill

f	o	r	c	e	h	f
f	o	r	d	c	g	o
b	g	d	r	n	h	r
s	t	o	r	k	j	m
c	c	o	r	d	m	p
s	c	f	k	g	l	o
s	f	o	r	g	e	r
g	o	r	g	e	n	t

Read each group of letters. Put a slash between the letters so the phrase makes sense. A word from the lesson is in each phrase. One has been done for you.

Making Sense

scorch/the/wood   seeastork

astrangeform   ahotforge

needstrongforce   sailintoport

fordacreek   tiewithcord

feelgreatscorn   asteepgorge

LESSON 12

Word Swap

Read each sentence to yourself as I read it out loud. Look at the underlined part in each sentence. Choose a word from the box below that can replace the underlined part. Write the word in the blank. One has been done for you.

| cord force ~~ford~~ forge form gorge port scorch scorn stork |

1. The hikers decided to <u>walk through</u> the small stream. _____**ford**_____

2. The river ran through a <u>rocky valley</u>. _____

3. A hot iron might <u>burn</u> clothes. _____

4. The artist used a <u>furnace</u> so she could bend the metal. _____

5. A <u>tall bird</u> makes its home in a pond near our house. _____

6. The wind made the sand dune into a strange <u>shape</u>. _____

7. A <u>thick string</u> held the stalks of corn together. _____

8. The queen felt <u>dislike</u> for the thieves her guards had caught.

    _____

9. During a storm, ships often head for a <u>safe place</u>. _____

10. It took a lot of <u>power</u> to move the huge rock. _____

Name _____

Word Wise

Listen to each word I say. Draw a circle around the word.

1.	grith	girth	girsh
2.	frim	firc	firm
3.	chirl	whirl	thirl
4.	whir	chir	whiv
5.	squarm	spuarn	squirm
6.	mirth	mirst	marth
7.	quilk	quirk	quenk
8.	stirk	smird	smirk
9.	irk	irt	isk
10.	shirk	slirk	stord

Word Meaning

Look at the word or words in the box. Listen as I read them. Draw a circle around the answer that means about the same as the word or words in the box.

1.	spin	whirl	curl	world
2.	strangeness	curve	quirk	skirt
3.	strong	form	from	firm
4.	fake smile	squirt	smirk	snack
5.	distance around	forth	girth	birth
6.	wiggle	squirm	storm	stem
7.	avoid	sharp	shirk	shirt
8.	hum	whip	fur	whir
9.	bother	dirt	irk	park
10.	happiness	month	hurt	mirth

LESSON 13

Word by Word

firm	solid or strong	**shirk**	to avoid doing something
girth	the distance around something	**smirk**	a fake smile
irk	to bother	**squirm**	to wiggle to get away
mirth	happiness	**whir**	a humming sound
quirk	a strange way of doing something	**whirl**	to spin quickly

Read each sentence to yourself as I read it out loud. Choose a word from the list above that fits best in each sentence. Only one word will fit best in each sentence. Write the word in the blank.

1. Lou's little brother would _____ him when friends came over.

2. Jenn was filled with _____ on her birthday.

3. Rachel didn't _____ any of her chores, even the hard ones.

4. The students had to measure the _____ of the log.

5. The baby started to _____. He wanted to crawl on the ground.

6. The dry ground was _____ compared to the wet sand.

7. The _____ on Billy's face showed he had forgotten his homework.

8. Juana heard a _____ as the birds flew over her head.

9. Phil had a _____. He liked to eat an apple before dinner.

10. The plane's propeller began to _____.

Name _____

Look at each word in the first column. It is missing one letter. The missing letter is in the second column. Decide where the missing letter fits and write the correct word in the blank. One has been done for you.

	Word	Missing Letter	
1.	ik	r	**irk**
2.	mirk	s	_____
3.	gith	r	_____
4.	shrk	i	_____
5.	hirl	w	_____
6.	fim	r	_____
7.	uirk	q	_____
8.	mirt	h	_____
9.	whr	i	_____
10.	squim	r	_____

Read each definition below as I read it out loud. Find the word in the box that means the opposite of the definition. Write the word in the blank beside the definition. One has been done for you.

Opposites

firm	girth	irk	mirth	quirk	shirk	smirk	~~squirm~~	whir	whirl

	Definition	Opposite
1.	To hold still	**squirm**
2.	To do a job quickly	_____
3.	To be nice to	_____
4.	A normal way to do things	_____
5.	Sadness	_____

Name_____

Read each question to yourself while I read it out loud. Think of the word from the lesson that best answers the question. Write the word on the line after the question. The words from the lesson are in the box.

firm   girth   irk   mirth   quirk   shirk   smirk   squirm   whir   whirl

1. What is a humming sound? _____

2. When you bother someone, what is it called? _____

3. If you avoid doing something, what is it called? _____

4. What do you call something that is solid? _____

5. What is a fake smile called? _____

6. What is a strange way to do something? _____

7. When you wiggle to get away, what is it called? _____

8. What is another word for happiness? _____

9. If you spin something quickly, what is it called? _____

10. What is the distance around something? _____

Did You Know?

If something is bothering you, it is called **irksome**. This is about the same as **bothersome**.

When you **whirl** something, you spin it around quickly. It may make a **whir** or humming sound as it spins.

Name _____

Listen to each word I say. Draw a circle around the word.

1.	frul	furl	furf
2.	hurl	harl	turl
3.	curge	surpe	surge
4.	brurt	blurt	blant
5.	curt	surt	curf
6.	barst	purst	burst
7.	hurk	lork	lurk
8.	urge	arge	urpe
9.	tarf	turf	tuth
10.	shurn	charn	churn

Look at the word or words in the box. Listen as I read them. Draw a circle around the answer that means about the same as the word or words in the box.

1.	sneak	lurk	bulb	luck
2.	grass	bush	tube	turf
3.	move quickly	serve	surge	stuck
4.	break	purse	purple	burst
5.	say quickly	blurt	bury	blue
6.	throw	hurt	hurl	burn
7.	shake up	churn	club	such
8.	persuade	turn	urge	large
9.	roll up	fur	full	furl
10.	rude	curt	curl	cure

LESSON 14

Word by Word

blurt	to say something without thinking	**hurl**	to throw hard
burst	to break quickly	**lurk**	to sneak around
churn	to stir or beat	**surge**	to move forward quickly
curt	rude	**turf**	thick grass
furl	to roll up cloth	**urge**	to tell someone to do something

Read each sentence to yourself as I read it out loud. Choose a word from the list above that fits best in each sentence. Only one word will fit best in each sentence. Write the word in the blank.

1. The catcher had to _____ the ball to second base.

2. The _____ on the soccer field is perfect for the game.

3. Tom would often _____ out the answer without raising his hand.

4. The wind made the flag _____ around the pole.

5. Mom had to _____ Peter to do his chores.

6. The balloon touched the thorny rose bush. It _____ into tiny pieces.

7. The raccoon would _____ in the shadows before sneaking to the garbage cans.

8. Gwen apologized for making a _____ remark to her friend.

9. At the end of the race, Lee tried to _____ in front of the other runners.

10. Long ago, people would _____ milk to make butter.

Read each question to yourself as I read it out loud. Circle the answer you think is correct. One has been done for you.

1. If you are rude, are you (curt) or **turf**?

2. If people sneak around, do they **blurt** or **lurk**?

3. If something moves forward, does it **surge** or **furl**?

4. If you mix something up, do you **churn** or **urge**?

5. If you throw something hard, do you **burst** or **hurl**?

Look at the Word Maze puzzle below. The letter *u* is missing from each word. Write the letter *u* where it belongs to complete each word. One has been done for you.

b	l	u	r	t			
		h		r	l		t
r		c		r	t		c
s					r		
t					r	f	r
s		r	g	e		g		t
	f		r	l		e		
l		r	k				

LESSON 14

Fix the Word

Read each definition to yourself as I read it out loud. Find the scrambled word that matches the definition. Draw a line from the definition to the correct scrambled word. Fix the word and write it on the line beside the scrambled word. One has been done for you.

to break quickly	rulf	_____
to say something without thinking	rnuhc	_____
rude	ruges	_____
to tell someone to do something	rbtus	**burst**
to roll up cloth	krul	_____
to mix	grue	_____
to throw hard	truc	_____
to move forward quickly	frut	_____
to sneak around	brult	_____
thick grass	luhr	_____

Did You Know?

Many professional sports teams play on artificial **turf**. It looks and feels a lot like real grass.

When a crowd moves ahead all at once, it is said to **surge** forward.

When someone is **curt**, they show rudeness by answering a question with too few words in a way that isn't very nice.

snarl	mar	girth	harm
whir	blurt	shirk	ford
scorch	smirk	stork	lurk
shard	stark	turf	barge
harsh	force	form	scorn
gnarl	urge	squirm	mirth
port	gorge	churn	burst
whirl	furl	quirk	irk
surge	curt	hurl	char
firm	cord	forge	tart

<u>Word Reading Directions:</u> **Read each word out loud. Start with the top row and read from left to right. Try to read quickly and correctly. If you aren't sure how to read a word, take your best guess. You may skip a word, but only if you can't read it at all. Just say "skip." Are you ready? You may begin.**

<u>Administration and Scoring Directions</u>: Begin timing when the student starts reading. Stop the assessment after one minute or if the student makes four errors in a row.

Put a check mark beside each word the student reads correctly. Draw a line through each word the student reads incorrectly or skips. Circle the last word the student reads within one minute. Record the correct number of words per minute in the space at the bottom of the page and on the Progress Monitoring Form on page 151.

Name_____   Date_____

snarl	mar	girth	harm
whir	blurt	shirk	ford
scorch	smirk	stork	lurk
shard	stark	turf	barge
harsh	force	form	scorn
gnarl	urge	squirm	mirth
port	gorge	churn	burst
whirl	furl	quirk	irk
surge	curt	hurl	char
firm	cord	forge	tart

<u>Word Meaning Directions</u>: **Listen to each word I say. In your own words, tell me what the word means. If you aren't sure what a word means, take your best guess. You may skip a word, but only if you don't have any idea what it means. Just say "skip." Are you ready? Let's begin.**

<u>Administration and Scoring Directions</u>: Read each word out loud. Start with the top row and read from left to right. Begin timing when you say the first word. Stop the assessment after one minute or if the student makes four errors in a row.

Put a check mark beside each word the student defines correctly. Draw a line through each word the student defines incorrectly or skips. Circle the last word the student attempts within one minute. Record the correct number of words per minute in the space at the bottom of the page and on the Progress Monitoring Form on page 151.

Name_____ Date_____

cord	stork	quirk	harsh
girth	curt	tart	shirk
scorn	urge	stark	smirk
squirm	port	gorge	form
shard	harm	whirl	irk
barge	forge	whir	firm
mar	gnarl	lurk	churn
char	snarl	ford	surge
turf	force	mirth	burst
scorch	furl	blurt	hurl

LESSON 15

Name_____

Read each word below. Choose a word from the box that means about the same as the word. Write the word in the blank. One has been done for you. The words from the lesson are at the bottom of the page. You will not use all the words.

On Your Own

grass _____**turf**_____   happiness _____

throw _____   narrow valley_____

spin _____   sneak around_____

string _____   cross stream _____

mix _____   flat boat _____

wiggle_____   sharp piece _____

shape _____   bother _____

growl _____   tall bird _____

barge	blurt	burst	char	churn
cord	curt	firm	force	ford
forge	form	furl	girth	gnarl
gorge	harm	harsh	hurl	irk
lurk	mar	mirth	port	quirk
scorch	scorn	shard	shirk	smirk
snarl	squirm	stark	stork	surge
tart	~~turf~~	urge	whir	whirl

Listen to each word I say. Draw a circle around the word.

1. merge   marge   werge
2. slern   sterv   stern
3. cerve   verve   verre
4. barm   berw   berm
5. perth   perch   parst
6. herb   lerd   herg
7. nerge   verge   varge
8. serse   vense   verse
9. swerve   sterce   swerse
10. barth   bersh   berth

Look at the word or words in the box. Listen as I read them. Draw a circle around the answer that means about the same as the word or words in the box.

1. | bed | earth   berry   berth
2. | energy | wave   verve   very
3. | sit | perch   torch   search
4. | long mound | dream   berm   bend
5. | strict | stern   storm   street
6. | plant | hire   hurt   herb
7. | edge | first   verge   range
8. | join | orange   merge   hinge
9. | part of song | verse   rinse   curve
10. | turn quickly | serve   swerve   sweep

LESSON 16

Word by Word

berm	long mound of dirt	**swerve**	to turn quickly
berth	bed in a ship or train	**verge**	edge of something or about to happen
herb	plant used in cooking	**verse**	part of a song or poem
merge	join together		
perch	to sit on something	**verve**	energy
stern	strict		

Read each sentence to yourself as I read it out loud. Choose a word from the list above that fits best in each sentence. Only one word will fit best in each sentence. Write the word in the blank.

1. The mountain guide was _____ about following safety rules.

2. The second _____ of the song was Todd's favorite.

3. The bulldozer made a _____ out of dirt.

4. The cheerleader was full of _____ and enthusiasm.

5. Lisa took the train from New York to California. She slept in a _____.

6. The tall pile of books was on the _____ of falling over.

7. The school bus had to _____ into a lane on the highway.

8. Every morning a blue jay would _____ on my windowsill.

9. Chris uses spices and a special _____ when he cooks chili.

10. The car had to _____ off the road to avoid the fallen branch.

Name_____

Look at the letters below. You can make at least six words from the lesson using the letters. You can use a letter more than once. Write each word you find on a line. Cross off the word from the list after you write it. One has been done for you.

b c e g h m p r s t w v

| berm berth herb merge perch stern ~~swerve~~ verge verse verve |

_____ swerve _____   _____

_____   _____

_____   _____

_____   _____

Read each question to yourself while I read it out loud. Write your answer on the line after each question.

1. What might you **perch** on? _____

_____

2. Where would you find an **herb**? _____

_____

3. When would you **swerve**? _____

_____

4. Where would someone **merge**? _____

_____

5. Who do you know who has lots of **verve**? _____

_____

LESSON 16

Word Scramble

Read each sentence to yourself. The underlined word has scrambled letters. Think about the word you can make from the letters. Write the word in the blank beside the sentence. One has been done for you.

1. The <u>trebh</u> on the train was very small. _____**berth**_____

2. The science and math clubs will <u>greme</u> soon. _____

3. This <u>svere</u> of the song is about new friends. _____

4. Sage is an <u>hreb</u> that is in many foods. _____

5. The officer was <u>nerst</u> when she spoke to the speeding driver. _____

6. Joan was on the <u>vreeg</u> of buying a new car. _____

7. Our school's band has lots of <u>reevv</u>. _____

8. A <u>ermb</u> along the road can cut down on noise. _____

9. A bird will sometimes <u>prech</u> on the roof of our house. _____

10. Roxie had to <u>versew</u> her bike around the big rock. _____

Did You Know?

The word **verge** means about the same as a word you learned before, **brink**. They both mean *edge*.

The word **herb** is sometimes pronounced without the beginning *h*. Parts of the plants in an **herb** garden are used to make food tasty.

You can remember that **stern** means **strict** because both words begin with st.

Name _____

Listen to each word I say. Draw a circle around the word.

1.	barl	tawl	bawl
2.	thaw	tham	staw
3.	blawn	bralt	brawn
4.	gauze	gauve	geaze
5.	hool	haul	kaul
6.	graw	gnaw	snaw
7.	hawn	parn	dawn
8.	vault	vealt	mault
9.	taunch	launch	leanch
10.	strawl	screal	scrawl

Word Meaning

Look at the word or words in the box. Listen as I read them. Draw a circle around the answer that means about the same as the word or words in the box.

1.	morning	dawn	aunt	down
2.	cloth for sores	graze	group	gauze
3.	start	lunch	launch	pinch
4.	protected room	laugh	built	vault
5.	strength	brawn	barn	because
6.	melt	thaw	straw	than
7.	cry	draw	bawl	bank
8.	chew	claw	paw	gnaw
9.	drag	fault	haul	fail
10.	write badly	cause	caught	scrawl

Name_____

bawl	to cry loudly	**launch**	to start something
brawn	strength	**scrawl**	to write badly
dawn	early morning	**thaw**	to melt
gauze	loose cloth to cover a sore	**vault**	a strong room to protect money or other valuables
gnaw	to chew		
haul	to pull or drag		

Read each sentence to yourself as I read it out loud. Choose a word from the list above that fits best in each sentence. Only one word will fit best in each sentence. Write the word in the blank.

1. The bank kept all of its money in a _____.

2. Rob had to _____ a note quickly on the back of an envelope.

3. Dad wanted the chicken to _____ so he took it out of the freezer.

4. The dog was happy to _____ on her bone all day long.

5. Raoul used a piece of _____ to cover the cut on his knee.

6. Gene woke up at _____ and saw the sun rise.

7. The baby started to _____ when his mother left the room.

8. Lucy needed all of her _____ to pick up the heavy box.

9. Simone had to _____ her sled all the way up the hill.

10. Scientists will _____ the rocket tomorrow morning.

Read each definition on the list. Think of the word from the lesson that matches the definition. Find each word in the grid. Draw a circle around the word and cross off the definition on the list. The words can go in any direction. One has been done for you.

Word Cross

- ~~to cry a lot~~
- great strength
- the very beginning of the day
- cloth to cover a cut
- to chew
- to pull or drag something
- to get something started
- to write so it is hard to read
- to melt
- a special room to protect valuable things

t	h	a	w	n	t	e
z	b	a	w	l	z	s
r	n	a	u	u	s	c
g	r	a	a	l	q	r
b	v	g	y	t	v	a
l	a	u	n	c	h	w
x	d	a	w	n	w	l

Read each group of letters. Put a slash between the letters so the phrase makes sense. A word from the lesson is in each phrase. One has been done for you.

Making Sense

show/some/brawn   haulacouch

launchaboat   scrawlanote

gnawanapple   bawlaboutit

needsomegauze   inavault

awakeatdawn   icewillthaw

LESSON 17

Word Swap

Read each sentence to yourself as I read it out loud. Look at the underlined part in each sentence. Choose a word from the box below that can replace the underlined part. Write the word in the blank. One has been done for you.

bawl	~~brawn~~	dawn	gauze	gnaw
haul	launch	scrawl	thaw	vault

1. The <u>strength</u> of the worker let him move the big pipe. _____**brawn**_____

2. The company will <u>put into the sea</u> its newest ship soon. _____

3. Matt's dog loves to <u>chew</u> on bones. _____

4. Mom covered Todd's cut with <u>loose cloth</u>. _____

5. Jill only had time to <u>write</u> a note to her dad. _____

6. The bank keeps its money in a <u>safe room</u> in the basement. _____

7. The baby will <u>cry loudly</u> when she is hungry. _____

8. The ice on the lake will <u>melt</u> in April. _____

9. Two of us were able to <u>drag</u> the old tire off the road. _____

10. The birds began to sing when <u>early morning</u> arrived. _____

Name _____

Listen to each word I say. Draw a circle around the word.

1.	foom	loom	lood
2.	trood	brood	brout
3.	frew	crev	crew
4.	gloom	ploom	groum
5.	troom	grood	groom
6.	swoop	shoop	swoip
7.	cloom	bloom	bloow
8.	loot	leat	lool
9.	hev	gew	hew
10.	sloop	cloop	slood

Look at the word or words in the box. Listen as I read them. Draw a circle around the answer that means about the same as the word or words in the box.

Word Meaning

1.	flower	bloom	block	boast
2.	group	stew	crawl	crew
3.	darkness	glove	gloom	goose
4.	cut	hen	few	hew
5.	bird babies	brood	droop	brook
6.	tool to make cloth	mood	loop	loom
7.	stolen money	loud	loot	hoop
8.	brush	grown	groom	ground
9.	sailboat	stood	scoop	sloop
10.	fly down	swoop	storm	troop

LESSON 18

Word by Word

bloom	a flower	**hew**	to cut with an axe
brood	babies of a bird or animal	**loom**	machine to make cloth
crew	team	**loot**	stolen money or things
gloom	darkness	**sloop**	a small sailboat
groom	to brush an animal	**swoop**	to fly down quickly

Read each sentence to yourself as I read it out loud. Choose a word from the list above that fits best in each sentence. Only one word will fit best in each sentence. Write the word in the blank.

1. The _____ on the rosebush was huge and colorful.

2. Patty was on a _____ that helped to clean the highways.

3. The stolen _____ was returned to the owners.

4. Jamie watched the hawk _____ to the ground looking for food.

5. The _____ was having a hard time sailing on the choppy water.

6. Randall had to _____ the logs to build the cabin.

7. The _____ of the night made it very hard for Sue to see.

8. Lester would _____ his dog outside to keep the fur out of the house.

9. The robin fed worms to her _____ .

10. The worker used the _____ to make beautiful cloth.

High Noon Vocabulary B: **Variant vowel pairs: ew, oo**

Name_____

Look at each word in the first column. It is missing one letter. The missing letter is in the second column. Decide where the missing letter fits and write the correct word in the blank. One has been done for you.

	Word	Missing Letter	
1.	soop	w	__swoop__
2.	cew	r	_____
3.	lom	o	_____
4.	rood	b	_____
5.	ew	h	_____
6.	blom	o	_____
7.	oot	l	_____
8.	goom	r	_____
9.	sloo	p	_____
10.	glom	o	_____

Read each definition below as I read it out loud. Find the word in the box that means the opposite of the definition. Write the word in the blank beside the definition. One has been done for you.

bloom brood crew gloom groom hew loom ~~loot~~ sloop swoop

Definition	**Opposite**
1. Money you earned	__loot__
2. One person working alone	_____
3. Lots of light	_____
4. To float up slowly	_____
5. A grown-up bird or animal	_____

LESSON 18

Word Quest

Read each question to yourself while I read it out loud. Think of the word from the lesson that best answers the question. Write the word on the line after the question. The words from the lesson are in the box.

bloom brood crew gloom groom hew loom loot sloop swoop

1. What are the babies of a bird called? _____

2. What is a group of workers called? _____

3. If you brush a dog, what is it called? _____

4. What would you call stolen things? _____

5. What is a machine that makes cloth? _____

6. What is it called to fly down quickly? _____

7. What is a small sailboat? _____

8. What is another word for darkness? _____

9. When you cut something with an axe, what is it called? _____

10. What is another name for a flower? _____

Did You Know?

Groom means "to brush an animal." The person who takes care of the animal, especially a horse, may also be called a **groom**.

Gloom means darkness. If a place is dark and not very nice, it is called **gloomy**.

If you look closely at a piece of cloth, you will see that the threads run in both directions and cross over and under. A **loom** is the machine that does this.

High Noon Vocabulary B: ***Variant vowel pairs: ew, oo***

Name_____

Listen to each word I say. Draw a circle around the word.

1.	mount	moust	rount
2.	stowl	scoil	scowl
3.	strout	sprout	sproun
4.	tound	bovnd	bound
5.	fowl	dowl	forl
6.	zow	voa	vow
7.	hout	pout	pouk
8.	crouch	clouch	cronch
9.	vound	mound	mornd
10.	ploch	pouch	poust

Look at the word or words in the box. Listen as I read them. Draw a circle around the answer that means about the same as the word or words in the box.

1.	small bag	pound	found	pouch
2.	look sad	boat	pout	pond
3.	grow	sprout	pound	sound
4.	bend down	count	bounce	crouch
5.	small hill	mound	hound	around
6.	climb up	meant	mount	bounce
7.	farm bird	foam	loaf	fowl
8.	sure to happen	bound	young	round
9.	a promise	tow	vow	sow
10.	look angry	score	scoop	scowl

LESSON 19

Word by Word

bound	sure to happen	**pouch**	a small bag
crouch	to squat down	**pout**	to look sad
fowl	a chicken or other farm bird	**scowl**	an angry look
mound	a small hill	**sprout**	to begin growing
mount	to climb up on something	**vow**	a promise

Read each sentence to yourself as I read it out loud. Choose a word from the list above that fits best in each sentence. Only one word will fit best in each sentence. Write the word in the blank.

1. Francis practiced the piano every day. He was _____ to get better.

2. Leo carried his marbles in a _____.

3. The _____ laid eggs that the farmer would sell.

4. Nina's face had a _____ after she heard the bad news.

5. Nick made a _____ that he would do his homework right after school.

6. The ants made a _____ with dirt from their nest.

7. Patricia had to _____ so she could see under the fence.

8. At camp, Gil learned how to _____ a horse.

9. All Todd could do was _____ when his team lost.

10. The plants started to _____ through the dirt.

LESSON 19

Which One?

Read each question to yourself as I read it out loud. Circle the answer you think is correct. One has been done for you.

1. If you squat down, do you **(crouch)** or **vow**?

2. Is a chicken a **pouch** or a **fowl**?

3. If something is sure to happen is it **bound** or **sprout**?

4. Is a sad look a **mound** or a **pout**?

5. If you climb up on something, do you **mount** or **scowl**?

Word Maze

Look at the Word Maze puzzle below. The letter _o_ is missing from each word. Write the letter _o_ where it belongs to complete each word. One has been done for you.

s	c	o	w	l		c	
p		v		w		r	
r				l	m		
		u	w			u	p
u			t		u	c	
t	f				n	h	u
	b		u	n	d		c
m		u	n	t			h

LESSON 19

Fix the Word

Read each definition to yourself as I read it out loud. Find the scrambled word that matches the definition. Draw a line from the definition to the correct scrambled word. Fix the word and write it on the line beside the scrambled word. One has been done for you.

a farm bird	ochup	_____
sure to happen	clows	_____
to squat down	lowf	**fowl**
to climb up on something	tupo	_____
an angry look	tumon	_____
a small hill	chuorc	_____
a promise	wov	_____
a small bag	noubd	_____
to look sad	truspo	_____
to begin growing	undom	_____

Did You Know?

Some animals have a built-in **pouch**. Kangaroos and koalas keep their babies in a **pouch**.

Sprout means "to begin growing." When plants first start growing, they are called **sprouts**. The **sprouts** of some plants are good to eat.

Word Reading

bawl	verve	vow	brood
scrawl	brawn	perch	gnaw
swoop	bloom	gauze	haul
thaw	launch	bound	berm
pout	swerve	loom	pouch
vault	dawn	berth	hew
gloom	sloop	scowl	herb
verge	sprout	crew	fowl
stern	mount	verse	loot
crouch	merge	mound	groom

LESSON 20

Word Reading

Word Reading Directions: Read each word out loud. Start with the top row and read from left to right. Try to read quickly and correctly. If you aren't sure how to read a word, take your best guess. You may skip a word, but only if you can't read it at all. Just say "skip." Are you ready? You may begin.

Administration and Scoring Directions: Begin timing when the student starts reading. Stop the assessment after one minute or if the student makes four errors in a row.

Put a check mark beside each word the student reads correctly. Draw a line through each word the student reads incorrectly or skips. Circle the last word the student reads within one minute. Record the correct number of words per minute in the space at the bottom of the page and on the Progress Monitoring Form on page 151.

Name_____ Date_____

bawl	verve	vow	brood
scrawl	brawn	perch	gnaw
swoop	bloom	gauze	haul
thaw	launch	bound	berm
pout	swerve	loom	pouch
vault	dawn	berth	hew
gloom	sloop	scowl	herb
verge	sprout	crew	fowl
stern	mount	verse	loot
crouch	merge	mound	groom

Word Reading Directions: Read each word out loud. Start with the top row and read from left to right. Try to read quickly and correctly. If you aren't sure how to read a word, take your best guess. You may skip a word, but only if you can't read it at all. Just say "skip." Are you ready? You may begin.

Administration and Scoring Directions: Begin timing when the student starts reading. Stop the assessment after one minute or if the student makes four errors in a row.

Put a check mark beside each word the student reads correctly. Draw a line through each word the student reads incorrectly or skips. Circle the last word the student reads within one minute. Record the correct number of words per minute in the space at the bottom of the page and on the Progress Monitoring Form on page 151.

Name_____ Date_____

merge	gauze	crew	pout
vow	mount	groom	perch
pouch	dawn	launch	bloom
berth	gloom	sloop	loom
thaw	brood	verge	fowl
berm	mound	scrawl	crouch
verve	vault	haul	scowl
loot	bawl	gnaw	stern
bound	swerve	hew	herb
swoop	sprout	brawn	verse

On Your Own

Name_____

Read each word below. Choose a word from the box that means about the same as the word. Write the word in the blank. One has been done for you. The words from the lesson are at the bottom of the page. You will not use all the words.

energy	**verve**	cut	_____
fly down	_____	join	_____
turn quickly	_____	melt	_____
strength	_____	chew	_____
flower	_____	promise	_____
darkness	_____	strict	_____
write badly	_____	morning	_____
stolen money	_____	cry	_____

bawl	berm	berth	bloom	bound
brawn	brood	crew	crouch	dawn
fowl	gauze	gloom	gnaw	groom
haul	herb	hew	launch	loom
loot	merge	mound	mount	perch
pouch	pout	scowl	scrawl	sloop
sprout	stern	swerve	swoop	thaw
vault	verge	verse	~~verve~~	vow

Name _____

Listen to each word I say. Draw a circle around the word.

1.	hoil	foil	foit
2.	toil	towl	koil
3.	woy	soy	siy
4.	voil	sool	soil
5.	poist	joist	jorst
6.	moist	monst	moich
7.	floy	plog	ploy
8.	coy	noy	cov
9.	holst	koist	hoist
10.	coil	noil	coul

Look at the word or words in the box. Listen as I read them. Draw a circle around the answer that means about the same as the word or words in the box.

1.	lift	hoist	toast	hitch
2.	thin metal	fool	foil	fold
3.	make loops	cone	cool	coil
4.	shy	bay	key	coy
5.	dirt	soar	soil	soup
6.	work	toil	boil	tone
7.	a kind of plant	toy	say	soy
8.	wet	meant	most	moist
9.	wood beam	join	joist	joy
10.	a trick	ploy	flow	plow

LESSON 21

Word by Word

coil	to wrap in loops	**moist**	a little wet
coy	shy	**ploy**	a trick to fool someone
foil	a thin sheet of metal	**soil**	dirt
hoist	to lift	**soy**	a kind of bean plant
joist	wood or metal that holds up a floor	**toil**	to work hard

Read each sentence to yourself as I read it out loud. Choose a word from the list above that fits best in each sentence. Only one word will fit best in each sentence. Write the word in the blank.

1. Mary was quiet and _____ around strangers.

2. Mr. Allan would _____ for hours fixing up his house.

3. Nancy made up a _____ to fool her friends.

4. Allison used _____ to wrap her sandwich.

5. Ms. Howard planted the seeds in the _____.

6. Beans from the _____ plant are tasty and good for you.

7. A wooden _____ in the basement held up the living room floor.

8. Louis cleaned the table with a _____ cloth.

9. Jorge remembered to _____ the hose after washing the car.

10. Rob used a rope to _____ the big chair onto the porch.

Look at the letters below. You can make at least six words from the lesson using the letters. You can use a letter more than once. Write each word you find on a line. Cross off the word from the list after you write it. One has been done for you.

c f h i j l m o p s t y

| coil | coy | foil | hoist | ~~joist~~ | moist | ploy | soil | soy | toil |

_____ **joist** _____   _____

_____   _____

_____   _____

_____   _____

_____   _____

In Your
Own Words

Read each question to yourself while I read it out loud. Write your answer on the line after each question.

1. What is something that is **moist**? _____

   _____

2. Where would you find a **joist**? _____

   _____

3. Where is the **soil** very good? _____

   _____

4. When is it fun to **toil**? _____

   _____

5. What might you **coil**? _____

   _____

LESSON 21

Word Scramble

Read each sentence to yourself. The underlined word has scrambled letters. Think about the word you can make from the letters. Write the word in the blank beside the sentence. One has been done for you.

1. Grandmother has some <u>yos</u> plants in her garden. _____**soy**_____

2. Carol helped Nick <u>thois</u> the box into the truck. _____

3. Fran's <u>poly</u> did not fool his little sister. _____

4. The leaves were <u>misot</u> from the fog. _____

5. My little brother is <u>yoc</u> around people he doesn't know. _____

6. The <u>sloi</u> in our yard is not very good for growing grass. _____

7. Dad wrapped the leftovers in <u>ifol</u>. _____

8. Each <u>iostj</u> under the floor was made of strong wood. _____

9. The family had to <u>toli</u> to fix up their house._____

10. It took a long time to <u>loic</u> the heavy rope. _____

Did You Know?

The beans of a **soy** plant are made into many of the foods you eat. They can even be made into something that looks and tastes like milk.

Moist means a little wet. **Moisture** means wetness. On a hot day, moisture forms on the outside of a cold glass.

Coil can be a noun and a verb. If a rope has been wrapped into loops, it is called a **coil**.

Name_____

Listen to each word I say. Draw a circle around the word.

1.	laiv	tair	lair
2.	snace	snare	sware
3.	hare	hane	kare
4.	mare	mase	sare
5.	smare	spare	spure
6.	flair	frair	flait
7.	flave	flare	flure
8.	grare	glave	glare
9.	pawe	pare	pire
10.	plare	blave	blare

Look at the word or words in the box. Listen as I read them. Draw a circle around the answer that means about the same as the word or words in the box.

1.	ability	flour	flair	flame
2.	extra	spoon	stain	spare
3.	female horse	maze	mare	care
4.	bright light	flare	stair	clear
5.	cut away	dare	pare	fair
6.	make noise	blare	share	shore
7.	angry look	drain	glides	glare
8.	trap	snore	snare	stare
9.	hiding place	bait	rail	lair
10.	animal like a rabbit	hare	hose	hail

*High Noon Vocabulary B: **Variant Vowel Patterns: air, are***

LESSON 22

Word by Word

blare	to make a loud noise	**mare**	a female horse
flair	ability	**soil**	dirt
flare	something that makes a bright light	**pare**	to remove the outside of something, like fruit
glare	an angry look	**snare**	a trap
hare	a kind of big rabbit	**spare**	extra
lair	an animal's hiding place		

Read each sentence to yourself as I read it out loud. Choose a word from the list above that fits best in each sentence. Only one word will fit best in each sentence. Write the word in the blank.

1. The ranger set a _____ to trap the possum. She would find it a new home.

2. Wendy helped to _____ the potatoes for dinner.

3. Sarah wanted to _____ at her friends, but she knew it was wrong.

4. The lion napped in his _____ to avoid the hot sun.

5. Sean kept a _____ tire in the trunk of his car.

6. The police officer lit a _____ to warn drivers of the accident.

7. The _____ had huge ears with black tips.

8. The horn will_____ to start the race.

9. Luis had a _____ for making his brother laugh.

10. The _____ stood by the stable with the other horses eating oats.

Read each definition on the list. Think of the word from the lesson that matches the definition. Find each word in the grid. Draw a circle around the word and cross off the definition on the list. The words can go in any direction. One has been done for you.

- ~~to make a loud noise~~
- a talent
- something that makes a bright light
- an angry look
- a kind of big rabbit
- where an animal hides or lives
- a female horse
- to cut away the outside of something
- a trap
- extra

s	n	a	r	e	e	m
g	p	h	a	r	e	b
l	a	a	a	l	r	l
a	r	m	r	i	h	a
r	e	i	a	e	f	r
e	a	l	k	j	g	e
l	f	l	a	r	e	d

Read each group of letters. Put a slash between the letters so the phrase makes sense. A word from the lesson is in each phrase. One has been done for you.

glare/at/them

ridethemare

lightaflare

heardtheblare

pareanorange

afasthare

setasnare

flairforcooking

asparepen

ahiddenlair

LESSON 22

Word Swap

Read each sentence to yourself as I read it out loud. Look at the underlined part in each sentence. Choose a word from the box below that can replace the underlined part. Write the word in the blank. One has been done for you.

| blare flair ~~flare~~ glare hare lair mare pare snare spare |

1. The plane dropped a <u>bright light</u> to help the search. _____**flare**_____

2. The <u>female horse</u> and her baby stood in the field._____

3. Gina gave her friend a <u>mean look</u>, but said she was sorry. _____

4. Long ago, people used a <u>trap</u> to catch their food. _____

5. The story took place in a dragon's <u>home</u>. _____

6. Beth has a <u>talent</u> for making people laugh. _____

7. Leon let Vickie use his <u>extra</u> pencil. _____

8. Some people <u>cut the skin from</u> an apple before eating it. _____

9. The <u>loud noise</u> of the truck's horn made us jump. _____

10. A big animal like a <u>rabbit</u> ran across the desert. _____

Listen to each word I say. Draw a circle around the word.

1.	gear	goor	jear
2.	loard	hourd	hoard
3.	hearn	yearn	yearp
4.	loce	kore	lore
5.	sear	vear	soir
6.	dore	bore	bove
7.	boam	boar	toar
8.	stear	slear	shear
9.	gourd	goird	gourp
10.	cire	cowe	core

Look at the word or words in the box. Listen as I read them. Draw a circle around the answer that means about the same as the word or words in the box.

1.	stuff	fear	gear	grin
2.	burn	sear	soar	tear
3.	want a lot	cream	earth	yearn
4.	center	more	core	roar
5.	drill a hole	bore	boom	bone
6.	part of a plant	group	gourd	heard
7.	stories	line	tore	lore
8.	wild pig	goat	boar	hope
9.	keep a lot	hoard	bounce	board
10.	cut	reach	shear	spear

*High Noon Vocabulary B: **Variant Vowel Patterns with r*** **89**

LESSON 23

Word by Word

boar	a wild pig	**hoard**	to keep a lot of something
bore	to make a hole with a drill	**lore**	stories or knowledge
core	the center of something	**sear**	to burn
gear	stuff	**shear**	to cut
gourd	a plant with a fruit like a cucumber	**yearn**	to want something very much

Read each sentence to yourself as I read it out loud. Choose a word from the list above that fits best in each sentence. Only one word will fit best in each sentence. Write the word in the blank.

1. Theresa would _____ for a new bicycle.

2. You shouldn't eat the _____ of a pear.

3. Gil had to _____ a hole in the wall with a drill.

4. Lance packed all of his hiking _____ in his backpack.

5. The farmer picked a _____ from a vine in her garden.

6. The mayor asked people not to _____ food during the storm.

7. The campers enjoyed hearing the forest _____ and other stories.

8. The wild _____ ate apples from the ground.

9. The rancher decided to _____ the sheep for their wool.

10. Lana wanted to _____ the steak on both sides on the grill.

Name _____

LESSON 23

Missing Letter

Look at each word in the first column. It is missing one letter. The missing letter is in the second column. Decide where the missing letter fits and write the correct word in the blank. One has been done for you.

	Word	Missing Letter	
1.	yean	r	__yearn__
2.	ger	a	_____
3.	ore	l	_____
4.	cre	o	_____
5.	sea	r	_____
6.	oard	h	_____
7.	boe	r	_____
8.	sear	h	_____
9.	gurd	o	_____
10.	boa	r	_____

Read each definition below as I read it out loud. Find the word in the box that means the opposite of the definition. Write the word in the blank beside the definition. One has been done for you.

| boar | ~~bore~~ core gear gourd hoard lore sear shear yearn |

Opposites

Definition	Opposite
1. To fix a hole	__bore__
2. A pet pig	_____
3. To care little for something	_____
4. To give things away	_____
5. The outside of something	_____

*High Noon Vocabulary B: **Variant Vowel Patterns with r*** 91

22

LESSON 23

Word Quest

Read each question to yourself while I read it out loud. Think of the word from the lesson that best answers the question. Write the word on the line after the question. The words from the lesson are in the box.

boar   bore   ~~core~~   gear   gourd   hoard   lore   sear   shear   yearn

1. What is the center of something? _____ **core** _____

2. What is another name for stories or knowledge? _____

3. What is a plant with fruit like cucumbers? _____

4. What is it called when you drill a hole? _____

5. What is another word for cut? _____

6. When you keep too much of something, what is it called? _____

7. If you burn something, what is it called? _____

8. What do you call a wild pig? _____

9. When you want something very much, what is it called? _____

10. What is another name for stuff? _____

Did You Know?

Here's a way to remember the meaning of two of the words from the lesson. You might have to **bore** to get to the **core** of something.

The word **hoard** means that someone is being selfish. People **hoard** things like food and water that are needed by other people.

Name_____

Listen to each word I say. Draw a circle around the word.

1.	strall	shrall	stroll
2.	tolp	toll	koll
3.	solt	colt	colp
4.	molt	mokt	rolt
5.	scholl	scrill	scroll
6.	bolt	hult	balt
7.	scild	scold	shold
8.	bold	bolp	beld
9.	holl	foll	poll
10.	jolt	polt	folt

Look at the word or words in the box. Listen as I read them. Draw a circle around the answer that means about the same as the word or words in the box.

1.	young horse	cold	cost	colt
2.	shake	jolt	both	felt
3.	vote	golf	doll	poll
4.	lose feathers	molt	moth	belt
5.	brave	pole	bold	fold
6.	payment	toll	tell	full
7.	roll of paper	spread	stretch	scroll
8.	say bad things	short	scold	score
9.	walk	swell	still	stroll
10.	lock part	gold	felt	bolt

*High Noon Vocabulary B: **Variant Vowel Patterns: ol-***

LESSON 24

Word by Word

bold	without fear	**scold**	to say bad things
bolt	part of a door lock		to a person
colt	a young horse	**scroll**	a roll of paper used
jolt	to shake hard		for writing long ago
molt	to lose feathers	**stroll**	to walk slowly
	or a shell	**toll**	the cost to use a
poll	a vote		road or bridge

Read each sentence to yourself as I read it out loud. Choose a word from the list above that fits best in each sentence. Only one word will fit best in each sentence. Write the word in the blank.

1. You have to pay a _____ to go over the bridge.

2. The scientists found an old _____ in the cave in the desert.

3. Dad had to _____ Chris because he almost hurt his little sister.

4. The bird will _____ in the spring and grow new feathers.

5. The teacher took a _____ of the students to find their favorite sports.

6. The _____ was almost as fast as the other horses.

7. Brooke and Amy took a _____ down the street to the park.

8. Lewis made sure to _____ the gate to make sure the animals didn't get out.

9. Kurt felt _____ and decided to jump off the high diving board.

10. The bus driver was careful not to _____ the passengers on the bumpy road.

Name _____

Read each question to yourself as I read it out loud. Circle the answer you think is correct. One has been done for you.

1. Is a young horse a **scroll** or a (**colt?**)

2. If you shake something hard, do you **jolt** or **stroll**?

3. Is a vote a **poll** or a **bolt**?

4. If you say bad things, do you **molt** or **scold**?

5. Is the cost of using a bridge a **toll** or a **bold**?

Look at the Word Maze puzzle below. The letters *ol* are missing from each word. Write the letters *ol* where they belong to complete each word. One has been done for you.

s	t	r	o	l	l		s
b			d				c
	b		t				r
s	c		d		c		
	t		l				
p		l				l	
j		t			t		
	m		t				

LESSON 24

Fix the Word

Read each definition to yourself as I read it out loud. Find the scrambled word that matches the definition. Draw a line from the definition to the correct scrambled word. Fix the word and write it on the line beside the scrambled word. One has been done for you.

the cost to use a road or bridge	oljt	_____
a roll of paper used for writing long ago	lorcsl	_____
without fear	tolm	_____
a young horse	oltb	_____
part of a door lock	lortsl	_____
to lose feathers or a shell	dolb	_____
to walk slowly	dolcs	_____
a vote	lotl	**toll**
to shake hard	lopl	_____
to say bad things to a person	tolc	_____

Did You Know?

The **bolt** in a lock is the piece of metal that slides from the door into the frame around the door.

When a bird **molts**, old feathers fall out and new feathers grow in.

The **scroll** was invented by Egyptians more than 4,000 years ago.

toll	mare	hare	colt
bore	flare	snare	hoist
bolt	blare	yearn	gear
scold	stroll	foil	boar
flair	hoard	shear	ploy
gourd	poll	spare	sear
coy	coil	molt	pare
toil	bold	lair	jolt
glare	scroll	soy	joist
moist	core	lore	soil

Word Reading Directions: Read each word out loud. Start with the top row and read from left to right. Try to read quickly and correctly. If you aren't sure how to read a word, take your best guess. You may skip a word, but only if you can't read it at all. Just say "skip." Are you ready? You may begin.

Administration and Scoring Directions: Begin timing when the student starts reading. Stop the assessment after one minute or if the student makes four errors in a row.

Put a check mark beside each word the student reads correctly. Draw a line through each word the student reads incorrectly or skips. Circle the last word the student reads within one minute. Record the correct number of words per minute in the space at the bottom of the page and on the Progress Monitoring Form on page 151.

Name_____ Date_____

toll	mare	hare	colt
bore	flare	snare	hoist
bolt	blare	yearn	gear
scold	stroll	foil	boar
flair	hoard	shear	ploy
gourd	poll	spare	sear
coy	coil	molt	pare
toil	bold	lair	jolt
glare	scroll	soy	joist
moist	core	lore	soil

<u>Word Meaning Directions</u>: **Listen to each word I say. In your own words, tell me what the word means. If you aren't sure what a word means, take your best guess. You may skip a word, but only if you don't have any idea what it means. Just say "skip." Are you ready? Let's begin.**

<u>Administration and Scoring Directions</u>: Read each word out loud. Start with the top row and read from left to right. Begin timing when you say the first word. Stop the assessment after one minute or if the student makes four errors in a row.

Put a check mark beside each word the student defines correctly. Draw a line through each word the student defines incorrectly or skips. Circle the last word the student attempts within one minute. Record the correct number of words per minute in the space at the bottom of the page and on the Progress Monitoring form on page 151.

Name_____ Date_____

core	yearn	lair	flair
hare	scroll	soil	snare
ploy	poll	stroll	blare
spare	coy	coil	shear
scold	colt	toil	jolt
boar	lore	bore	moist
mare	gourd	gear	molt
joist	toll	hoist	glare
foil	hoard	sear	pare
bolt	bold	flare	soy

On Your Own

Name_____

Read each word below. Choose a word from the box that means about the same as the word. Write the word in the blank. One has been done for you. The words from the lesson are at the bottom of the page. You will not use all the words.

stuff	**gear**	drill	_____
dirt	_____	female horse	_____
fearless	_____	cut	_____
extra	_____	make noise	_____
walk	_____	work	_____
young horse	_____	center	_____
stories	_____	trap	_____
damp	_____	lift	_____

blare	boar	bold	bolt	bore
coil	colt	core	coy	flair
flare	foil	~~gear~~	glare	gourd
hare	hoard	hoist	joist	jolt
lair	lore	mare	moist	molt
pare	ploy	poll	scold	scroll
sear	shear	snare	soil	soy
spare	stroll	toil	toll	yearn

Name_____

Listen to each word I say. Draw a circle around the word.

1.	stull	stall	stalt
2.	rind	vind	rand
3.	haltz	walth	waltz
4.	bind	dind	binb
5.	glind	grend	grind
6.	kalt	halt	halg
7.	posd	pust	post
8.	squall	squalp	stuall
9.	vild	mild	milp
10.	tost	hoth	host

Look at the word or words in the box. Listen as I read them. Draw a circle around the answer that means about the same as the word or words in the box.

1.	storm	small	quart	squall
2.	pole	post	lost	pond
3.	nice	tile	mild	dime
4.	rub into pieces	grind	grape	bring
5.	dance	health	waltz	watch
6.	person having a party	torn	horn	host
7.	outside of fruit	rind	wind	sink
8.	stop	belt	hunt	halt
9.	space with walls	shade	stall	sharp
10.	tie	bind	bank	wind

LESSON 26

Word by Word

bind	to tie together	**post**	a pole that holds up a building
grind	to crush or rub into small pieces	**rind**	the outside of some fruit or vegetable
halt	to stop	**squall**	a sudden storm
host	someone who is having a party	**stall**	an enclosed space
mild	nice, not too hot or cold	**waltz**	a dance from long ago

Read each sentence to yourself as I read it out loud. Choose a word from the list above that fits best in each sentence. Only one word will fit best in each sentence. Write the word in the blank.

1. Some horses are in the barn. Each one is in a _____.

2. This _____ holds up the roof of the porch.

3. Cars _____ at the stop sign at the end of the street.

4. Rosa will _____ the flower stems with string.

5. It was raining hard. The children came inside during the _____.

6. The music was playing. People began to _____.

7. Mother has to _____ the coffee beans.

8. The _____ gave the guests very fancy snacks.

9. The _____ of the orange is a part you don't eat.

10. Today's weather is _____. It is not too hot or too cold.

Name_____

Look at the letters below. You can make at least six words from the lesson using the letters. You can use a letter more than once. Write each word you find on a line. Cross off the word from the list after you write it. One has been done for you.

a b d g h i l n o p q r s t u w z

bind	grind	halt	host	mild
post	~~rind~~	squall	stall	waltz

_____**rind**_____   _____

_____   _____

_____   _____

_____   _____

_____   _____

Read each question to yourself while I read it out loud. Write your answer on the line after each question.

1. What might you **grind**? _____

_____

2. What would you do in a **squall**? _____

_____

3. When would you be a **host**? _____

_____

4. What has a **rind**? _____

_____

5. What might someone **bind**? _____

_____

LESSON 26

Word Scramble

Read each sentence to yourself. The underlined word has scrambled letters. Think about the word you can make from the letters. Write the word in the blank beside the sentence. One has been done for you.

1. The bride and groom danced a <u>zwalt</u> at the wedding. _____**waltz**_____

2. Gina was sure to thank the <u>thos</u> after the party. _____

3. Even though it was winter, the day was <u>dlim</u> and sunny. _____

4. Traffic had to <u>thal</u> because of an accident. _____

5. Each corner of the roof was held up with a heavy <u>opst</u>._____

6. The <u>drin</u> of the watermelon was bright green. _____

7. Jane will <u>bnid</u> the newspapers with string before recycling them.

   _____

8. Each horse has its own <u>slatl</u> in the barn. _____

9. A big machine will <u>dring</u> the wheat into flour. _____

10. A <u>lalusq</u> rocked the small boat back and forth. _____

Did You Know?

A **mild** day is nice. It's not too hot or cold. When food is **mild**, it is not too spicy. A person who is **mild** is kind and does not become angry easily.

A **squall** is a noisy storm. **Squall** has another meaning as a verb. When a baby cries and makes a lot of noise, the baby is **squalling**.

Name_____

Word Wise

Listen to each word I say. Draw a circle around the word.

1.	shigh	thigh	frigh
2.	fraught	traught	frausth
3.	pright	glight	plight
4.	flaght	clight	flight
5.	froight	freight	freinth
6.	sight	cight	sught
7.	oight	ought	orght
8.	steigh	sloogh	sleigh
9.	sigh	sagh	righ
10.	songht	sought	pought

Word Meaning

Look at the word or words in the box. Listen as I read them. Draw a circle around the answer that means about the same as the word or words in the box.

1.	should	ought	enough	south
2.	looked for	thought	sound	sought
3.	danger	tight	plight	right
4.	things carried	straight	friend	freight
5.	what is seen	sight	eight	light
6.	breathe out	high	sigh	sign
7.	air travel	flake	might	flight
8.	full of	caught	fraught	laugh
9.	big sled	sleigh	sleeve	weigh
10.	leg part	fight	thing	thigh

LESSON 27

Word by Word

flight	a trip through the air	**sight**	something that is seen
fraught	full of	**sleigh**	a kind of big sled
freight	things that are carried	**sought**	looked for
ought	should	**thigh**	the top of the leg
plight	a dangerous situation		above the knee
sigh	to let out a deep breath		

Read each sentence to yourself as I read it out loud. Choose a word from the list above that fits best in each sentence. Only one word will fit best in each sentence. Write the word in the blank.

1. You really _____ to help your mom clean up.

2. It takes two horses to pull that _____.

3. We went to Hawaii by plane. The _____ was very long.

4. Juan _____ his lost kitten.

5. The train carries _____ across the country.

6. The _____ of the lost hikers improved when they found water.

7. Grandmother enjoyed the _____ of the children playing.

8. Rob fell down. Now he has a big bruise on his _____.

9. The trip through the jungle was _____ with danger.

10. People often _____ when they are tired.

Read each definition on the list. Think of the word from the lesson that matches the definition. Find each word in the grid. Draw a circle around the word and cross off the definition on the list. The words can go in any direction. One has been done for you.

- ~~flying~~
- having a lot of
- things that are shipped
- should
- a kind of a problem
- to breathe out and make a sound
- what you see
- a big sled, usually pulled by animals
- looked for
- the top of your leg

a	s	i	g	h	t	f	t
p	l	i	g	h	t	r	n
d	o	u	g	h	t	a	i
v	b	u	g	h	n	u	g
c	o	i	t	h	i	g	h
s	l	e	i	g	h	h	r
f	r	e	i	g	h	t	o

Read each group of letters. Put a slash between the letters so the phrase makes sense. A word from the lesson is in each phrase. One has been done for you.

sought/a/friend   oughttostudy

freightonships   fraughtwithproblems

tosighloudly   inaplight

alongflight   hurtherthigh

pullthesleigh   afunnysight

LESSON 27

Word Swap

Read each sentence to yourself as I read it out loud. Look at the underlined part in each sentence. Choose a word from the box below that can replace the underlined part. Write the word in the blank. One has been done for you.

flight	fraught	freight	~~ought~~	plight
sigh	sight	sleigh	sought	thigh

1. Store owners <u>are required</u> to get the snow off the sidewalk.

   _____**ought**_____

2. The surfers <u>looked for</u> the place with the best waves._____

3. The <u>view</u> of their new house made the family happy. _____

4. The explorers' journey was <u>filled</u> with danger. _____

5. The children rode in a <u>big sled</u> pulled by a horse. _____

6. Jed let out a <u>deep breath</u> after making the basket. _____

7. A truck full of <u>goods to be sold</u> turned over on the highway. _____

8. Hal wrapped tape around his <u>leg above the knee</u>. _____

9. The <u>trip by plane</u> to Alaska took a long time. _____

10. The <u>dangerous situation</u> of the people was big news. _____

Did You Know?

The muscles in your **thigh** are the strongest muscles in your body. The **bone** in your **thigh** is the longest bone in your body.

A **sleigh** is similar to another word you learned before, **sledge**. A **sleigh** is bigger than a sled, and a **sledge** is bigger than a **sleigh**.

Name_____

Listen to each word I say. Draw a circle around the word.

1.	trief	broaf	brief
2.	shriek	striek	shrief
3.	saige	riege	siege
4.	wield	vield	woild
5.	dier	tier	tien
6.	poir	pier	piem
7.	gield	yiend	yield
8.	tierce	fierce	fource
9.	pierve	dierce	pierce
10.	grief	glief	graif

Look at the word or words in the box. Listen as I read them. Draw a circle around the answer that means about the same as the word or words in the box.

1.	use a weapon	field	wield	weld
2.	scream	shriek	streak	shrink
3.	violent	horse	fence	fierce
4.	put a hole in	pierce	scarce	course
5.	sadness	thief	grin	grief
6.	give up	held	yield	yard
7.	row	tier	tiny	team
8.	short	chief	brief	leaf
9.	attack	stage	hinge	siege
10.	platform near water	pine	pier	year

Name_____

brief	short	**shriek**	to scream
fierce	strong and violent	**siege**	to surround a place
grief	sadness		and attack it
pier	a kind of dock	**tier**	a layer or row
	in the water	**wield**	to use a weapon or tool
pierce	to put a hole in	**yield**	to give up

Read each sentence to yourself as I read it out loud. Choose a word from the list above that fits best in each sentence. Only one word will fit best in each sentence. Write the word in the blank.

1. Boats are tied at the _____.

2. Ann gave out a _____ when her team won.

3. Jan sat in the third _____ of seats at the show.

4. Lucy was slowing down. She had to _____ to the faster runner.

5. The trip was too _____. We wanted to stay longer.

6. When the king died, the people felt _____.

7. The army planned a _____ of the city.

8. A knight had to learn to _____ a sword.

9. The _____ winds blew the trees over.

10. The nurse used a small needle to _____ the blister.

Look at each word in the first column. It is missing one letter. The missing letter is in the second column. Decide where the missing letter fits and write the correct word in the blank.

	Word	Missing Letter	
1.	perce	i	**pierce**
2.	tie	r	_____
3.	sriek	h	_____
4.	ield	y	_____
5.	firce	e	_____
6.	sege	i	_____
7.	rief	g	_____
8.	wied	l	_____
9.	brie	f	_____
10.	ier	p	_____

Read each definition below as I read it out loud. Find the word in the box that means the opposite of the definition. Write the word in the blank beside the definition. One has been done for you.

brief	fierce	grief	pier	pierce
shriek	siege	tier	wield	~~yield~~

Definition	Opposite
1. To fight on	**yield**
2. Weak	_____
3. Happiness	_____
4. Long	_____
5. To be quiet	_____

LESSON 28

Word Quest

brief	fierce	grief	pier	pierce
shriek	siege	tier	wield	yield

Read each question to yourself while I read it out loud. Think of the word from the lesson that best answers the question. Write the word on the line after the question. The words from the lesson are in the box.

1. What is a kind of dock? _____

2. What is a kind of attack?_____

3. What word means strong and violent? _____

4. When you give up, what do you do? _____

5. When you put a hole in something, what do you do? _____

6. If you use a tool, what is it called? _____

7. What is another word for short? _____

8. What is another word for a layer or row? _____

9. What do you call a high scream? _____

10. If you are sad, what do you feel? _____

Did You Know?

An animal like a lion or tiger might be called **fierce**. A big storm might also be called **fierce**.

The seats in a sports stadium are arranged in **tiers**.

A **shriek** is usually a loud, high scream.

Name _____

Listen to each word I say. Draw a circle around the word.

1.	vein	veir	voin
2.	pren	prey	priy
3.	roin	reiv	rein
4.	fread	tread	treap
5.	weign	reing	reign
6.	dread	dreaf	cread
7.	shealth	stealph	stealth
8.	dealm	realm	healm
9.	feign	geign	feigh
10.	reil	veil	veit

Look at the word or words in the box. Listen as I read them. Draw a circle around the answer that means about the same as the word or words in the box.

Word Meaning

1.	feel afraid	dread	bread	spread
2.	thin cloth	real	very	veil
3.	area	realm	meal	meant
4.	walk	ready	tread	treat
5.	hunted animal	tray	prey	trip
6.	strap	rein	roam	ring
7.	secret movement	wealth	stream	stealth
8.	pretend	feign	fright	front
9.	body part	fine	vine	vein
10.	time of ruling	screen	reign	sign

LESSON 29

Word by Word

dread	to feel afraid	**stealth**	doing something quietly or secretly
feign	to pretend		
prey	an animal hunted by another animal	**tread**	to walk on and crush
		veil	thin cloth worn over the head or face
realm	the area ruled by a king or queen		
		vein	part of the body that carries blood
reign	the time a king or queen rules		
rein	a rope or strap to control a horse		

Read each sentence to yourself as I read it out loud. Choose a word from the list above that fits best in each sentence. Only one word will fit best in each sentence. Write the word in the blank.

1. Kate held the _____ in her hands to control the horse.

2. Matt will _____ to be hurt in the play.

3. The small _____ was ruled by a kind queen.

4. A _____ takes blood back to the heart.

5. George had studied hard and did not _____ the test.

6. A hawk hunts for _____ to feed its babies.

7. The hikers _____ on leaves that had fallen from the trees.

8. King John's _____ lasted for over thirty years.

9. The photographers used _____ to get close to the deer.

10. The bride is wearing a long white dress and a _____.

Read each question to yourself as I read it out loud. Circle the answer you think is correct. One has been done for you.

1. When something is done secretly, is it **prey** or **stealth?**

2. If you pretend, do you **feign** or **tread?**

3. Is the part of the body that carries blood a **reign** or a **vein?**

4. Would you control a horse with a **rein** or a **veil?**

5. Is an area ruled by a queen a **dread** or a **realm?**

Look at the Word Maze puzzle below. The letter _e_ is missing from each word. Write the letter _e_ where it belongs to complete each word. One has been done for you.

s	t	e	a	l	t	h		
	r		i	n				t
v		i	n		m	p	d	r
				l		r	r	
i			a					a
l					y	a	d	
	r		i	g	n		d	
		f		i	g	n		

LESSON 29

Fix the Word

Read each definition to yourself as I read it out loud. Find the scrambled word that matches the definition. Draw a line from the definition to the correct scrambled word. Fix the word and write it on the line beside the scrambled word. One has been done for you.

a rope or strap to control a horse	lamre	_____
an animal that is hunted by another animal	ivel	_____
to walk on and crush	eniv	_____
thin cloth worn over the head or face	giner	_____
part of the body that carries blood	inre	**rein**
to feel afraid	sheltat	_____
doing something quietly or secretly	ginef	_____
to pretend	redat	_____
the area ruled by a king or queen	radde	_____
the time a king or queen rules	yerp	_____

Did You Know?

If you do something secretly, you are being **stealthy**.

Most of the time, a horse is controlled with two **reins**, one on each side of its head.

A **veil** is usually so thin that you can see through it.

grind	pierce	squall	grief
fierce	sigh	feign	waltz
siege	plight	flight	pier
host	thigh	reign	dread
post	freight	veil	stealth
stall	wield	brief	vein
sight	sleigh	realm	rein
mild	tier	shriek	prey
fraught	yield	tread	rind
ought	sought	bind	halt

Word Reading

<u>**Word Reading Directions**</u>**: Read each word out loud. Start with the top row and read from left to right. Try to read quickly and correctly. If you aren't sure how to read a word, take your best guess. You may skip a word, but only if you can't read it at all. Just say "skip." Are you ready? You may begin.**

<u>Administration and Scoring Directions</u>: Begin timing when the student starts reading. Stop the assessment after one minute or if the student makes four errors in a row.

Put a check mark beside each word the student reads correctly. Draw a line through each word the student reads incorrectly or skips. Circle the last word the student reads within one minute. Record the correct number of words per minute in the space at the bottom of the page and on the Progress Monitoring Form on page 151.

Name_____ Date_____

grind	pierce	squall	grief
fierce	sigh	feign	waltz
siege	plight	flight	pier
host	thigh	reign	dread
post	freight	veil	stealth
stall	wield	brief	vein
sight	sleigh	realm	rein
mild	tier	shriek	prey
fraught	yield	tread	rind
ought	sought	bind	halt

Word Meaning Directions: Listen to each word I say. In your own words, tell me what the word means. If you aren't sure what a word means, take your best guess. You may skip a word, but only if you don't have any idea what it means. Just say "skip." Are you ready? Let's begin.

Administration and Scoring Directions: Read each word out loud. Start with the top row and read from left to right. Begin timing when you say the first word. Stop the assessment after one minute or if the student makes four errors in a row.

Put a check mark beside each word the student defines correctly. Draw a line through each word the student defines incorrectly or skips. Circle the last word the student attempts within one minute. Record the correct number of words per minute in the space at the bottom of the page and on the Progress Monitoring form on page 151.

Name_____ Date_____

sought	flight	shriek	post
squall	yield	halt	feign
stealth	wield	thigh	plight
brief	sight	sleigh	veil
host	grief	mild	prey
dread	bind	fierce	ought
pierce	stall	pier	realm
rind	grind	waltz	fraught
reign	freight	vein	rein
siege	tier	sigh	tread

On Your Own

Name_____

Read each word below. Choose a word from the box that means about the same as the word. Write the word in the blank. One has been done for you. The words from the lesson are at the bottom of the page. You will not use all the words.

dance	**waltz**	pretend	_____
fear	_____	layer	_____
storm	_____	sadness	_____
short	_____	give up	_____
violent	_____	scream	_____
full of	_____	hunted animal	_____
looked for	_____	tie	_____
stop	_____	sled	_____

bind	brief	dread	feign	fierce
flight	fraught	freight	grief	grind
halt	host	mild	ought	pier
pierce	plight	post	prey	realm
reign	rein	rind	shriek	siege
sigh	sight	sleigh	sought	squall
stall	stealth	thigh	tier	tread
veil	vein	~~waltz~~	wield	yield

Name_____

Word Wise

Listen to each word I say. Draw a circle around the word.

1.	marshy	marthy	warshy
2.	foomy	foavy	foamy
3.	tuzzy	fuzzy	funzy
4.	drasty	drifty	drafty
5.	grumpy	trumpy	grimpy
6.	thilly	chilly	chinny
7.	crirky	quilty	quirky
8.	witty	vitty	wotty
9.	thristy	thrifty	throfty
10.	messy	wessy	mesty

Word Meaning

Look at the word or words in the box. Listen as I read them. Draw a circle around the answer that means about the same as the word or words in the box.

1.	clever	windy	witty	gritty
2.	spending wisely	thrifty	swiftly	handy
3.	cool	holly	chilly	silly
4.	unhappy	grumpy	bumpy	group
5.	bubbly	heavy	roaming	foamy
6.	hairy	funny	puzzle	fuzzy
7.	not neat	money	messy	grassy
8.	strange	quirky	quickly	quietly
9.	breezy	drifted	after	drafty
10.	swampy	march	marshy	worthy

LESSON 31

Word by Word

chilly	a little cold	**grumpy**	unhappy
drafty	breezy or a little windy	**marshy**	swampy
		messy	not neat
foamy	with lots of bubbles on the surface	**quirky**	strange
		thrifty	using money wisely
fuzzy	covered with tiny hairs	**witty**	smart or clever

Read each sentence to yourself as I read it out loud. Choose a word from the list above that fits best in each sentence. Only one word will fit best in each sentence. Write the word in the blank.

1. Larry is _____ when he has to wake up too early.

2. There are toys everywhere. The family room is kind of _____.

3. Anna is _____. She likes to buy things on sale.

4. Fall is here. It is getting _____ outside.

5. Susan used bubble bath in the tub. The water got all _____.

6. Carmen tells clever stories. Her friends say she is very _____.

7. The old barn was _____ because of loose boards.

8. A peach has a _____ skin.

9. The field became _____ when the stream flooded.

10. The motor is _____. Sometimes it works, but sometimes it doesn't.

Name_____

Look at the letters below. You can make at least six words from the lesson using the letters. You can use a letter more than once. Write each word you find on a line. Cross off the word from the list after you write it. One has been done for you.

a c e f h i k l m q r s t u w y z

chilly	drafty	foamy	fuzzy	grumpy
~~marshy~~	messy	quirky	thrifty	witty

_____**marshy**_____   _____

_____   _____

_____   _____

_____   _____

_____   _____

Read each question to yourself while I read it out loud. Write your answer on the line after each question.

1. Who do you know who is **messy**? _____

_____

2. What might be **foamy**? _____

_____

3. When are people **grumpy**? _____

_____

4. What is something that is **fuzzy**? _____

_____

5. What animals live in **marshy** places? _____

_____

Name _____

Read each sentence to yourself. The underlined word has scrambled letters. Think about the word you can make from the letters. Write the word in the blank beside the sentence. One has been done for you.

1. The hotel was <u>kriyuq</u> with lots of strange rooms. _____**quirky**_____

2. The baby chicks were cute and <u>zufyz</u>. _____

3. Dustin was tired and felt <u>murgpy</u>. _____

4. The <u>frithty</u> family bought only things they needed. _____

5. The open window made the room <u>fradyt</u>. _____

6. Sandy cleaned up the <u>smesy</u> room before her friends came over.

    _____

7. Grandfather made <u>moafy</u> hot chocolate for us. _____

8. Ducks liked to build nests in the <u>shymar</u> field. _____

9. Karen is <u>tiwty</u> because of the clever things she says. _____

10. The day was too <u>lichly</u> to play outside. _____

Did You Know?

Quirky means strange in a good or interesting way.

A **thrifty** person is not greedy. A **thrifty** person spends money wisely. A greedy person is selfish.

Chilly is almost cold, but not quite cold. **Drafty** is almost windy, but not quite windy.

Name_____

Listen to each word I say. Draw a circle around the word.

1.	sterved	swerved	swelved
2.	merged	merted	menged
3.	clouched	crouthed	crouched
4.	swoiped	swooped	shooped
5.	pared	pased	paren
6.	housted	hoisted	hoished
7.	pierned	pourced	pierced
8.	grieved	grouved	griexed
9.	stuirmed	squirved	squirmed
10.	barled	cawled	bawled

Look at the word or words in the box. Listen as I read them. Draw a circle around the answer that means about the same as the word or words in the box.

1.	was sad	grieved	believed	grabbed
2.	joined	melted	charged	merged
3.	bent down	touched	crouched	crossed
4.	cried	crawled	pulled	bawled
5.	turned quickly	served	swerved	sweetened
6.	put a hole in	pierced	poured	placed
7.	lifted	toasted	heated	hoisted
8.	flew down	slipped	swooped	scooped
9.	wiggled	stormed	mined	squirmed
10.	cut	pared	dared	paid

High Noon Vocabulary B: **Final -d, -ed** 125

LESSON 32

Word by Word

bawled	cried	**pared**	removed the outside
crouched	squatted down	**pierced**	put a hole through
grieved	became sad	**squirmed**	wiggled to get away
hoisted	lifted up	**swerved**	turned quickly
merged	joined together	**swooped**	flew down quickly

Read each sentence to yourself as I read it out loud. Choose a word from the list above that fits best in each sentence. Only one word will fit best in each sentence. Write the word in the blank.

1. D'Neece _____ the carrots before slicing them.

2. The baby _____ when it got hungry.

3. A big crane _____ the air conditioner up to the roof.

4. A thorn _____ Carol's glove.

5. Dan fell when he _____ on his bike.

6. Willie's cat _____ under a bush.

7. Two lanes of traffic _____ into one.

8. Her puppy _____ when Laura picked it up.

9. A large bird _____ from the tree to the ground.

10. Everyone _____ when their town was flooded.

Read each definition on the list. Think of the word from the lesson that matches the definition. Find each word in the grid. Draw a circle around the word and cross off the definition on the list. The words can go in any direction. One has been done for you.

- ~~cried~~
- hunched down
- felt very sad
- lifted up
- joined together
- removed the outside
- put a hole through
- wiggled to get away
- turned quickly
- flew down quickly

g	p	i	e	r	c	e	d	i
r	c	w	p	a	r	e	d	s
i	r	s	y	n	t	o	s	q
e	o	u	w	s	v	f	w	u
v	u	r	i	e	d	l	o	i
e	c	o	l	i	r	o	o	r
d	h	a	e	k	f	v	p	m
m	e	r	g	e	d	t	e	e
h	d	b	a	w	l	e	d	d

Read each group of letters. Put a slash between the letters so the phrase makes sense. A word from the lesson is in each phrase. One has been done for you.

the/baby/bawled

grievedaboutit

carsmergedcarefully

piercedherears

abirdswooped

hoistedthelog

heparedpotatoes

shecroucheddown

thepuppysquirmed

adriverswerved

LESSON 32

Word Swap

Read each sentence to yourself as I read it out loud. Look at the underlined part in each sentence. Choose a word from the box below that can replace the underlined part. Write the word in the blank. One has been done for you.

| bawled | crouched | grieved | hoisted | ~~merged~~ |
| pared | pierced | squirmed | swerved | swooped |

1. The two small companies <u>joined</u> into one bigger company.

   _____**merged**_____

2. The sharp rock <u>put a hole in</u> the air mattress. _____

3. The people <u>became sad</u> when they heard the bad news. _____

4. The baby <u>cried loudly</u> until his father picked him up. _____

5. The kitten <u>wiggled</u> when I tried to pick it up. _____

6. Two of the workers <u>lifted</u> the couch onto the truck. _____

7. The bats <u>flew down</u> near the pond to catch insects. _____

8. The truck <u>turned quickly</u> to avoid the ice. _____

9. Dad <u>cut the skin from</u> the potatoes before cooking them. _____

10. Martina <u>bent down</u> to get a good look at the lizard. _____

*High Noon Vocabulary B: **Final -d, -ed***

Listen to each word I say. Draw a circle around the word.

1.	prainly	plainly	ploinly
2.	mildly	mindly	maldly
3.	nightly	hightly	naghtly
4.	veekly	mookly	meekly
5.	firmly	tirmly	firtly
6.	laintly	faintly	fainthy
7.	briefly	criefly	triefly
8.	soldly	bildly	boldly
9.	grumly	glumly	glusly
10.	peftly	dertly	deftly

Look at the word or words in the box. Listen as I read them. Draw a circle around the answer that means about the same as the word or words in the box.

1.	gently	coldly	mildly	slowly
2.	dimly	gladly	exactly	faintly
3.	quickly	brightly	deftly	lovely
4.	not proudly	meekly	family	nearly
5.	sadly	really	silly	glumly
6.	bravely	quietly	boldly	smelly
7.	shortly	briefly	darkly	safely
8.	simply	finally	plainly	neatly
9.	every night	hilly	clearly	nightly
10.	strongly	firmly	lonely	hardly

Name_____

LESSON 33

Word by Word

boldly	without fear	**glumly**	sadly
briefly	for a short time	**meekly**	quietly and not proudly
deftly	quickly and smoothly	**mildly**	gently
faintly	dimly or quietly	**nightly**	every night
firmly	solidly or strongly	**plainly**	simply, not fancy

Read each sentence to yourself as I read it out loud. Choose a word from the list above that fits best in each sentence. Only one word will fit best in each sentence. Write the word in the blank.

1. Carla brushes her teeth _____ before going to bed.

2. Lights glowed _____ from the distant city.

3. The brave animal tamer _____ walked into the lion's cage.

4. Steven held the bat _____ so it wouldn't slip out of his hands.

5. Betty answered _____. She wasn't sure about her answer.

6. Mark dressed _____, but he really looked great.

7. There was not much time. The driver could only stop _____ for lunch.

8. The little girl did not get her way. She sat _____ in a corner.

9. Ned spoke _____ to calm the horse.

10. Mother knows how to sew. She _____ fixed the torn coat.

Name_____

LESSON 33

Missing Letter

Look at each word in the first column. It is missing one letter. The missing letter is in the second column. Decide where the missing letter fits and write the correct word in the blank. One has been done for you.

	Word	Missing Letter	
1.	eftly	d	**deftly**
2.	aintly	f	_____
3.	midly	l	_____
4.	painly	l	_____
5.	biefly	r	_____
6.	glumy	l	_____
7.	ightly	n	_____
8.	fimly	r	_____
9.	mekly	e	_____
10.	bodly	l	_____

Opposites

Read each definition below as I read it out loud. Find the word in the box that means the opposite of the definition. Write the word in the blank beside the definition. One has been done for you.

boldly	briefly	deftly	faintly	firmly
glumly	meekly	mildly	~~nightly~~	plainly

Definition	**Opposite**
1. Every day	**nightly**
2. Strongly	_____
3. Happily	_____
4. For a long time	_____
5. Brightly	_____

High Noon Vocabulary B: Final -ly **131**

LESSON 33

boldly	briefly	deftly	faintly	firmly
glumly	meekly	mildly	nightly	plainly

Read each question to yourself while I read it out loud. Think of the word from the lesson that best answers the question. Write the word on the line after the question. The words from the lesson are in the box.

1. If something is done in a short time, what is it called? _____

2. What word means about the same as sadly? _____

3. What word describes a sound you can barely hear? _____

4. If you do something gently, how do you do it? _____

5. What is another word for fearlessly? _____

6. What word means every night? _____

7. What word means not proudly? _____

8. What word means quickly and smoothly? _____

9. If something is done simply, what is it called? _____

10. What is something held strongly? _____

Did You Know?

The word **deftly** is often used to tell about skills you do with your hands like juggling.

Nightly means every night, just like **daily** means every day.

The most famous use of the word **boldly** was in the introduction to the television show Star Trek: "To boldly go where no man has gone before."

Name_____

Listen to each word I say. Draw a circle around the word.

1. shelves   stelves   shrelves
2. palves   ralves   calves
3. crieves   thieves   smieves
4. nalves   halves   hoves
5. scartes   sharves   scarves
6. loaves   looves   loares
7. elmes   elves   eldes
8. krives   kniles   knives
9. teaves   leaves   leares
10. hooves   fooves   hoodes

Word Meaning

Look at the word or words in the box. Listen as I read them. Draw a circle around the answer that means about the same as the word or words in the box.

1. | cutting tools | wolves   hives   knives
2. | tree parts | braves   leaves   caves
3. | magical people | elves   saves   waves
4. | horse feet | gloves   hooves   moves
5. | storage places | curves   serves   shelves
6. | people who steal | nerves   thieves   solves
7. | neck warmers | doves   proves   scarves
8. | parts of things | halves   wives   stoves
9. | baby cows | coves   calves   carves
10. | bread shapes | lives   dives   loaves

Name _____

LESSON 34

Word by Word

calves	calf, a young cow or bull	**scarves**	scarf, cloth worn around the neck
elves	elf, a magical person	**shelves**	shelf, a board on which things are stored
hooves	hoof, the foot of some animals, like a horse		
knives	knife, a cutting tool	**thieves**	thief, somebody who steals things
leaves	leaf, part of a tree		
loaves	loaf, the shape in		
halves	half, part of a whole thing		

Read each sentence to yourself as I read it out loud. Choose a word from the list above that fits best in each sentence. Only one word will fit best in each sentence. Write the word in the blank.

1. The police are looking for some _____.

2. Be careful. The _____ are sharp.

3. The _____ of bread are ready to come out of the oven.

4. All the _____ in the library are filled with books.

5. Many trees lose their _____ in the fall.

6. The farmer brought the _____ into the barn.

7. The horse's _____ made deep prints in the sand.

8. Sheridan cut the apple into two equal _____.

9. Jean read a fairy tale about _____.

10. Grandmother made woolen _____ for all of the family.

Name_____

Read each question to yourself as I read it out loud. Circle the answer you think is correct. One has been done for you.

1. Are boards on which things are stored (shelves) or **thieves**?

2. Are the feet of a horse **halves** or **hooves**?

3. Are things you wear around your neck **scarves** or **loaves**?

4. Are magical people **leaves** or **elves**?

5. Are young cows **knives** or **calves**?

Look at the Word Maze puzzle below. The letters e and s are missing from each word. Write the letters e and s where they belong to complete each word.

c	a	l	v	e	s	s	s
e	l	v				c	h
h	o	o	v			a	e
k	n	i	v			r	l
l	e	a	v			v	v
l	o	a	v				
h	a	l	v				
t	h	i	e	v			

Name_____

LESSON 34

Fix the Word

Read each definition to yourself as I read it out loud. Find the scrambled word that matches the definition. Draw a line from the definition to the correct scrambled word. Fix the word and write it on the line beside the scrambled word. One has been done for you.

young cows or bulls	selvah	_____
cloth worn around the neck	valees	_____
feet of some animals like a horse or deer	revacss	_____
cutting tools	claves	**calves**
the shapes in which bread is baked	hevites	_____
parts of a tree	leves	_____
magical people	slevhes	_____
people who steal things	vohose	_____
two equal parts of something	avoles	_____
boards on which things are stored	viknes	_____

Did You Know?

Calves are not only farm animals. **Calf** is also the name of the back part of your leg, below the knee.

The **hooves** of animals are like the fingernals or toenails of people or the claws of animals.

The singular form of **loaves** is **loaf**. In addition to meaning the shape of bread, **loaf** also means to be lazy and waste time.

Word Reading

plainly	messy	chilly	hooves
meekly	thrifty	drafty	quirky
swooped	foamy	boldly	nightly
hoisted	firmly	scarves	loaves
calves	shelves	grumpy	elves
mildly	faintly	fuzzy	squirmed
glumly	grieved	pared	swerved
knives	thieves	briefly	leaves
rooves	crouched	witty	pierced
merged	bawled	marshy	deftly

Word Reading Directions: Read each word out loud. Start with the top row and read from left to right. Try to read quickly and correctly. If you aren't sure how to read a word, take your best guess. You may skip a word, but only if you can't read it at all. Just say "skip." Are you ready? You may begin.

Administration and Scoring Directions: Begin timing when the student starts reading. Stop the assessment after one minute or if the student makes four errors in a row.

Put a check mark beside each word the student reads correctly. Draw a line through each word the student reads incorrectly or skips. Circle the last word the student reads within one minute. Record the correct number of words per minute in the space at the bottom of the page and on the Progress Monitoring Form on page 151.

Name_____ Date_____

plainly	messy	chilly	hooves
meekly	thrifty	drafty	quirky
swooped	foamy	boldly	nightly
hoisted	firmly	scarves	loaves
calves	shelves	grumpy	elves
mildly	faintly	fuzzy	squirmed
glumly	grieved	pared	swerved
knives	thieves	briefly	leaves
halves	crouched	witty	pierced
merged	bawled	marshy	deftly

<u>Word Meaning Directions</u>: **Listen to each word I say. In your own words, tell me what the word means. If you aren't sure what a word means, take your best guess. You may skip a word, but only if you don't have any idea what it means. Just say "skip." Are you ready? Let's begin.**

<u>Administration and Scoring Directions</u>: Read each word out loud. Start with the top row and read from left to right. Begin timing when you say the first word. Stop the assessment after one minute or if the student makes four errors in a row.

Put a check mark beside each word the student defines correctly. Draw a line through each word the student defines incorrectly or skips. Circle the last word the student attempts within one minute. Record the correct number of words per minute in the space at the bottom of the page and on the Progress Monitoring form on page 151.

Name_____ Date_____

bawled	boldly	briefly	calves
chilly	crouched	deftly	drafty
elves	faintly	firmly	foamy
fuzzy	glumly	grieved	grumpy
halves	hoisted	hooves	knives
leaves	loaves	marshy	meekly
merged	messy	mildly	nightly
pared	pierced	plainly	quirky
scarves	shelves	squirmed	swerved
swooped	thieves	thrifty	witty

Name _____

On Your Own

Read each word below. Choose a word from the box that means about the same as the word. Write the word in the blank. One has been done for you. The words from the lesson are at the bottom of the page. You will not use all the words.

flew down   **swooped**   became sad   _____

cold   _____   without fear   _____

turned quickly _____   strange   _____

smart   _____   cried   _____

joined   _____   lifted   _____

breezy   _____   unhappy   _____

swampy   _____   gently   _____

simply   _____   not neat   _____

bawled	boldly	briefly	calves	chilly
crouched	deftly	drafty	elves	faintly
firmly	foamy	fuzzy	glumly	grieved
grumpy	halves	hoisted	hooves	knives
leaves	loaves	marshy	meekly	merged
messy	mildly	nightly	pared	pierced
plainly	quirky	scarves	shelves	squirmed
swerved	~~swooped~~	thieves	thrifty	witty

LESSON 1

Word Wise – page 1
1. rill
2. dill
3. pal
4. fad
5. ban
6. sap
7. wit
8. deck
9. bid
10. peck

Word Meaning
1. dill
2. peck
3. ban
4. sap
5. pal
6. bid
7. deck
8. fad
9. rill
10. wit

Word by Word – page 2
1. pal
2. deck
3. dill
4. ban
5. bid
6. wit
7. fad
8. sap
9. peck
10. rill

Word Find – page 3
Answers may vary. All of the words listed except **sap**.

In Your Own Words
Answers may vary.

Word Scramble – page 4
1. dill
2. fad
3. sap
4. wit
5. ban
6. rill
7. deck
8. peck
9. bid
10. lad

LESSON 2

Word Wise – page 5
1. lob
2. lull
3. dock
4. nod
5. moss
6. fog
7. odd
8. buck
9. bud
10. pug

Word Meaning
1. fog
2. moss
3. lull
4. pug
5. bud
6. odd
7. nod
8. dock
9. lob
10. buck

Word by Word – page 6
1. buck
2. bud
3. nod
4. dock
5. fog
6. pug
7. moss
8. lull
9. lob
10. odd

Word Cross – page 7

l	m	o	s	s	k
u	b	d	o	c	k
l	n	b	u	d	f
l	o	b	c	d	o
o	d	d	p	u	g

Making Sense
run/and/buck
soft/green/moss
lull/the/horse
lob/a/ball
a/friendly/pug
the/thick/fog
a/tiny//bud
a/wooden/dock
an/odd/sound
nod/her/head

Word Swap – page 8
1. bud
2. fog
3. lull
4. odd
5. moss
6. buck
7. pug
8. lob
9. nod
10. dock

LESSON 3

Word Wise – page 9
1. zeal
2. quake
3. pane
4. heal
5. vain
6. jeer
7. keen
8. meek
9. heed
10. gape

Word Meaning
1. heed
2. quake
3. meek
4. vain
5. gape
6. keen
7. pane
8. jeer
9. heal
10. zeal

Word by Word – page 10
1. heal
2. jeer
3. gape
4. meek
5. pane
6. zeal
7. keen
8. quake
9. heed
10. vain

Missing Letter – page 11
1. vain
2. keen
3. heal
4. pane
5. zeal
6. gape
7. meek
8. jeer
9. quake
10. heed

Opposites
1. gape
2. keen
3. meek
4. zeal
5. heal

Word Quest – page 12
1. heed
2. keen
3. heal
4. pane
5. meek
6. keen
7. gape
8. quake
9. jeer
10. vain

LESSON 4

Word Wise – page 13
1. mule
2. quite
3. sole
4. code
5. due
6. fine
7. jute
8. lime
9. cope
10. pose

Word Meaning
1. cope
2. pose
3. mule
4. sole
5. lime
6. jute
7. quite
8. due
9. code
10. fine

Word by Word – page 14
1. due
2. pose
3. quite
4. mule
5. sole
6. code
7. fine
8. cope
9. lime
10. jute

Which One? – page 15
1. fine
2. lime
3. mule
4. cope
5. due

Word Maze – page 15

d	u	e		f	i	n	e	
	c	o	p	e				
c	o	d	e		j	u	t	e
l	i	m	e		m	u	l	e
q	u	i	t	e	p	o	s	e
		s	o	l	e			

Fix the Word – page 16

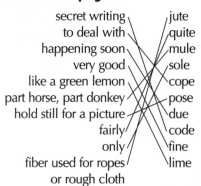

secret writing — code
to deal with — cope
happening soon — due
very good — fine
like a green lemon — lime
part horse, part donkey — mule
hold still for a picture — pose
fairly — quite
only — sole
fiber used for ropes or rough cloth — jute

ANSWER KEY

On Your Own – page 20

friend **pal**	shake **quake**
male deer **buck**	mist **fog**
too proud **vain**	forbid **ban**
make better **heal**	sharp **keen**
kind of dog **pug**	strange **odd**
plant part **bud**	throw **lob**
small stream **rill**	stare **gape**
piece of glass **pane**	listen to **heed**

LESSON 6

Word Wise – page 21

1. brink
2. pang
3. slang
4. cling
5. prank
6. flank
7. dank
8. prong
9. plank
10. link

Word Meaning

1. slang
2. prank
3. dank
4. flank
5. brink
6. pang
7. link
8. prong
9. cling
10. plank

Word by Word – page 22

1. prank
2. prong
3. dank
4. cling
5. brink
6. plank
7. flank
8. pang
9. slang
10. link

Word Find – page 23

Answers may vary but all of the words are found.

In Your Own Words

Answers may vary.

Word Scramble – page 24

1. slang
2. prong
3. link
4. prank
5. pang
6. brink
7. plank
8. cling
9. flank
10. dank

LESSON 7

Word Wise – page 25

1. hutch
2. thatch
3. clutch
4. latch
5. botch
6. sketch
7. snatch
8. fetch
9. notch
10. batch

Word Meaning – page 25 cont'd.

1. botch
2. fetch
3. notch
4. latch
5. batch
6. snatch
7. hutch
8. sketch
9. clutch
10. thatch

Word by Word – page 26

1. batch
2. hutch
3. sketch
4. thatch
5. botch
6. latch
7. clutch
8. notch
9. fetch
10. snatch

Word Cross – page 27

Making Sense

made/a/sketch	clutch/the/bag
a/pretty/hutch	close/the/latch
botch/the/job	fix/the/thatch
cut/a/notch	batch/of/cookies
fetch/a/stick	snatch/an/apple

Word Swap – page 28

1. botch
2. sketch
3. fetch
4. thatch
5. latch
6. batch
7. snatch
8. notch
9. hutch
10. clutch

LESSON 8

Word Wise – page 29

1. knead
2. wrath
3. wring
4. scent
5. gnat
6. gnu
7. knit
8. wren
9. knack
10. scene

Word Meaning

1. knack
2. gnu
3. wren
4. scene
5. knit
6. wring
7. wrath
8. gnat
9. scent
10. knead

Word by Word – page 30

1. knit
2. wrath
3. knack
4. wren
5. gnu
6. scene
7. knead
8. gnat
9. scent
10. wring

Missing Letter – page 31

1. scent
2. wrath
3. knack
4. scene
5. knead
6. gnu
7. wren
8. wring
9. gnat
10. knit

Opposites

1. knack
2. wrath
3. wring
4. knead
5. scent

Word Quest – page 32

1. knead
2. gnu
3. scent
4. knit
5. wren
6. gnat
7. wrath
8. knack
9. wring
10. scene

LESSON 9

Word Wise – page 33

1. hedge
2. ridge
3. lodge
4. pledge
5. budge
6. sledge
7. ledge
8. dodge
9. grudge
10. trudge

Word Meaning

1. dodge
2. ridge
3. hedge
4. sledge
5. budge
6. grudge
7. lodge
8. trudge
9. ledge
10. pledge

Word by Word – page 34

1. dodge
2. ledge
3. hedge
4. sledge
5. budge
6. pledge
7. trudge
8. lodge
9. grudge
10. ridge

Which One – page 35

1. pledge
2. trudge
3. hedge
4. lodge
5. ledge

ANSWER KEY

Word Maze – page 35

s	l	e	d	g	e			h
	t	r	u	d	g	e		e
b	u	d	g	e			r	d
	d	o	d	g	e		i	g
g	r	u	d	g	e		d	e
l	e	d	g	e			g	
l	o	d	g	e			e	
	p	l	e	d	g	e		

Fix the Word – page 36

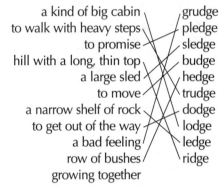

a kind of big cabin — lodge
to walk with heavy steps — trudge
to promise — pledge
hill with a long, thin top — ridge
a large sled — sledge
to move — budge
a narrow shelf of rock — ledge
to get out of the way — dodge
a bad feeling — grudge
row of bushes growing together — hedge

LESSON 10 – Progress Monitoring

On Your Own – page 40

anger **wrath**
straw **thatch**
piece of chain **link**
small cut **notch**
promise **pledge**
small bug **gnat**
row of bushes **hedge**
sharp pain **pang**

draw **sketch**
cabin **lodge**
grab **snatch**
damp **dank**
edge **brink**
bunch **batch**
rock shelf **ledge**
nice smell **scent**

LESSON 11

Word Wise – page 41

1. gnarl
2. snarl
3. stark
4. shard
5. harsh
6. harm
7. tart
8. barge
9. mar
10. char

Word Meaning

1. char
2. mar
3. harsh
4. gnarl
5. tart
6. snarl
7. stark
8. barge
9. shard
10. harm

Word by Word – page 42

1. mar
2. snarl
3. shard
4. tart
5. gnarl
6. barge
7. stark
8. harm
9. harsh
10. char

Word Find – page 43

Answers may vary. All of the words listed except **shard**.

In Your Own Words

Answers may vary.

Word Scramble – page 44

1. tart
2. harsh
3. char
4. mar
5. harm
6. stark
7. shard
8. gnarl
9. snarl
10. barge

LESSON 12

Word Wise – page 45

1. gorge
2. cord
3. scorch
4. scorn
5. port
6. forge
7. force
8. stork
9. ford
10. form

Word Meaning

1. port
2. gorge
3. force
4. form
5. ford
6. forge
7. stork
8. scorn
9. scorch
10. cord

Word by Word – page 46

1. cord
2. force
3. forge
4. stork
5. ford
6. form
7. port
8. gorge
9. scorn
10. scorch

Word Cross – page 47

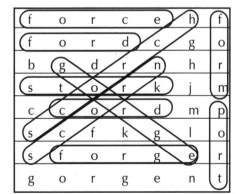

Making Sense

scorch/the/wood
a/strange/form
need/strong/force
ford/a/creek
feel/great/scorn

see/a/stork
a/hot/forge
sail/into/port
tie/with/cord
a/steep/gorge

Word Swap – page 48

1. ford
2. gorge
3. scorch
4. forge
5. stork
6. form
7. cord
8. scorn
9. port
10. force

LESSON 13

Word Wise – page 49

1. girth
2. firm
3. whirl
4. whir
5. squirm
6. mirth
7. quirk
8. smirk
9. irk
10. shirk

Word Meaning

1. whirl
2. quirk
3. firm
4. smirk
5. girth
6. squirm
7. shirk
8. whirl
9. irk
10. mirth

Word by Word – page 50

1. irk
2. mirth
3. shirk
4. girth
5. squirm
6. firm
7. smirk
8. whir
9. quirk
10. whirl

Missing Letter – page 51

1. irk
2. smirk
3. girth
4. shirk
5. whirl
6. firm
7. quirk
8. mirth
9. whir
10. squirm

Opposites

1. squirm
2. shirk
3. irk
4. quirk
5. mirth

Word Quest – page 52

1. whir
2. irk
3. shirk
4. firm
5. smirk
6. quirk
7. squirm
8. mirth
9. whirl
10. girth

LESSON 14

Word Wise – page 53

1. furl
2. hurl
3. surge
4. blurt
5. curt
6. burst
7. lurk
8. urge
9. turf
10. churn

Word Meaning

1. lurk
2. turf
3. surge
4. burst
5. blurt
6. hurl
7. churn
8. urge
9. furl
10. curt

Word by Word – page 54

1. hurl
2. turf
3. blurt
4. furl
5. urge
6. burst
7. lurk
8. curt
9. surge
10. churn

Which One? – page 55

1. curt
2. lurk
3. surge
4. churn
5. hurl

Word Maze

b	l	u	r	t			
u		h	u	r	l		t
r		c	u	r	t		u	c
s					u	r	u
t					r	f	r
s	u	r	g	e		g		t
	f	u	r	l		e	
l	u	r	k				

Fix the Word – page 56

to break quickly — furl
to say something
without thinking — chum
rude
to tell someone to — surge
do something — burst
to roll up cloth — lurk
a friend — urge
to throw hard — curt
move forward quickly — turf
to sneak around — blurt
thick grass — hurl

LESSON 15 – Progress Monitoring

On Your Own – page 60

grass **turf**
throw **hurl**
spin **whirl**
string **cord**
mix **churn**
wiggle **squirm**
shape **form**
growl **snarl**

happiness **mirth**
narrow valley **gorge**
sneak around **lurk**
cross stream **ford**
flat boat **barge**
sharp piece **shard**
bother **irk**
tall bird **stork**

LESSON 16

Word Wise – page 61

1. merge
2. stern
3. verve
4. berm
5. perch
6. herb
7. verge
8. verse
9. swerve
10. berth

Word Meaning

1. berth
2. verve
3. perch
4. berm
5. stern
6. herb
7. verge
8. merge
9. verse
10. swerve

Word by Word – page 62

1. stern
2. verse
3. berm
4. verve
5. berth
6. verge
7. merge
8. perch
9. herb
10. swerve

Word Find – page 63

Answers may vary.
All of the words listed except **stern**.

In Your Own Words

Answers may vary.

Word Scramble – page 64

1. berth
2. merge
3. verse
4. herb
5. stern
6. verge
7. verve
8. berm
9. perch
10. swerve

LESSON 17

Word Wise – page 65

1. bawl
2. thaw
3. brawn
4. gauze
5. haul
6. gnaw
7. dawn
8. vault
9. launch
10. scrawl

Word Meaning

1. dawn
2. gauze
3. launch
4. vault
5. brawn
6. thaw
7. bawl
8. gnaw
9. haul
10. scrawl

Word by Word – page 66

1. vault
2. scrawl
3. thaw
4. gnaw
5. gauze
6. dawn
7. bawl
8. brawn
9. haul
10. launch

Word Cross – page 67

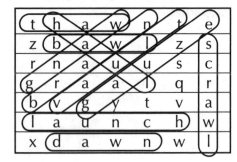

Making Sense

show/some/brawn
launch/a/boat
gnaw/an/apple
need/some/gauze
awake/at/dawn

haul/a/couch
scrawl/a/note
bawl/about/it
in/a/vault
ice/will/thaw

Word Swap – page 68

1. brawn
2. launch
3. gnaw
4. gauze
5. scrawl
6. vault
7. bawl
8. thaw
9. haul
10. dawn

LESSON 18

Word Wise – page 69

1. loom
2. brood
3. crew
4. gloom
5. groom
6. swoop
7. bloom
8. loot
9. hew
10. sloop

Word Meaning

1. bloom
2. crew
3. gloom
4. hew
5. brood
6. loom
7. loot
8. groom
9. sloop
10. swoop

LESSON 18 cont'd.
Word by Word – page 70
1. bloom
2. crew
3. loot
4. swoop
5. sloop
6. hew
7. gloom
8. groom
9. brood
10. loom

Missing Letter – page 71
1. swoop
2. crew
3. loom
4. brood
5. hew
6. bloom
7. loot
8. groom
9. sloop
10. gloom

Opposites
1. loot
2. crew
3. gloom
4. swoop
5. brood

Word Quest – page 72
1. brood
2. crew
3. groom
4. loot
5. loom
6. swoop
7. sloop
8. gloom
9. hew
10. bloom

LESSON 19
Word Wise – page 73
1. mount
2. scowl
3. sprout
4. bound
5. fowl
6. vow
7. pout
8. crouch
9. mound
10. pouch

Word Meaning
1. pouch
2. pout
3. sprout
4. crouch
5. mound
6. mount
7. fowl
8. bound
9. vow
10. scowl

Word by Word – page 74
1. bound
2. pouch
3. fowl
4. scowl
5. vow
6. mound
7. crouch
8. mount
9. pout
10. sprout

Which One? – page 75
1. crouch
2. fowl
3. bound
4. pout
5. mount

LESSON 19 cont'd.
Word Maze – page 75

s	c	o	w	l		c	
p		v	o	w		r	
r			l	m	o		
o		u	w		o	u	p
u			t		u	c	o
t	f				n	h	u
	b	o	u	n	d		c
m	o	u	n	t			h

Fix the Word – page 76

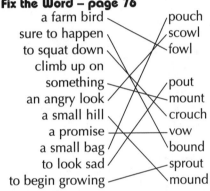

a farm bird — fowl
sure to happen — bound
to squat down — crouch
climb up on — mount
something — sprout
an angry look — scowl
a small hill — mound
a promise — vow
a small bag — pouch
to look sad — pout
to begin growing — sprout

(words: pouch, scowl, fowl, pout, mount, crouch, vow, bound, sprout, mound)

LESSON 20 – Progress Monitoring
On Your Own – page 80

energy **verve**
fly down **swoop**
turn quickly **swerve**
strength **brawn**
flower **bloom**
darkness **gloom**
write badly **scrawl**
stolen money **loot**

cut **hew**
join **merge**
melt **thaw**
chew **gnaw**
promise **vow**
strict **stern**
morning **dawn**
cry **bawl**

LESSON 21
Word Wise – page 81
1. foil
2. toil
3. soy
4. soil
5. joist
6. moist
7. ploy
8. coy
9. hoist
10. coil

Word Meaning
1. hoist
2. foil
3. coil
4. coy
5. soil
6. toil
7. soy
8. moist
9. joist
10. ploy

LESSON 21 cont'd.
Word by Word – page 82
1. coy
2. toil
3. ploy
4. foil
5. soil
6. soy
7. joist
8. moist
9. coil
10. hoist

Word Find – page 83
Answers may vary but all of the words are found.

In Your Own Words
Answers may vary.

Word Scramble – page 84
1. soy
2. hoist
3. ploy
4. moist
5. coy
6. soil
7. foil
8. joist
9. toil
10. coil

LESSON 22
Word Wise – page 85
1. lair
2. snare
3. hare
4. mare
5. spare
6. flair
7. flare
8. glare
9. pare
10. blare

Word Meaning
1. flair
2. spare
3. mare
4. flare
5. pare
6. blare
7. glare
8. snare
9. lair
10. hare

Word by Word – page 86
1. snare
2. pare
3. glare
4. lair
5. spare
6. flare
7. hare
8. blare
9. flair
10. mare

Word Cross – page 87

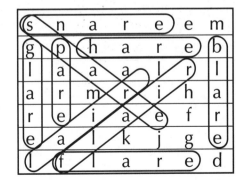

ANSWER KEY

LESSON 23

Word Wise – page 89
1. gear
2. hoard
3. yearn
4. lore
5. sear
6. bore
7. boar
8. shear
9. gourd
10. core

Making Sense
glare/at/them   a/fast/hare
ride/the/mare   set/a/snare
light/a/flare   flair/for/cooking
heard/the/blare   a/spare/pen
pare/an/orange   a/hidden/lair

Word Swap – page 88
1. flare
2. mare
3. glare
4. snare
5. lair
6. flair
7. spare
8. pare
9. blare
10. hare

Word Meaning – page 89
1. gear
2. sear
3. yearn
4. core
5. bore
6. gourd
7. lore
8. boar
9. hoard
10. shear

Word by Word – page 90
1. yearn
2. core
3. bore
4. gear
5. gourd
6. hoard
7. lore
8. boar
9. shear
10. sear

Missing Letter – page 91
1. yearn
2. gear
3. lore
4. core
5. sear
6. hoard
7. bore
8. shear
9. gourd
10. boar

Opposites
1. bore
2. boar
3. yearn
4. hoard
5. core

Word Quest – page 92
1. core
2. lore
3. gourd
4. bore
5. shear
6. hoard
7. sear
8. boar
9. yearn
10. gear

LESSON 24

Word Wise – page 93
1. stroll
2. toll
3. colt
4. molt
5. scroll
6. bolt
7. scold
8. bold
9. poll
10. jolt

Word Meaning
1. colt
2. jolt
3. poll
4. molt
5. bold
6. toll
7. scroll
8. scold
9. stroll
10. bolt

Word by Word – page 94
1. toll
2. scroll
3. scold
4. molt
5. poll
6. colt
7. stroll
8. bolt
9. bold
10. jolt

Which One? – page 95
1. colt
2. jolt
3. poll
4. scold
5. toll

Word Maze

s	t	r	o	l	l		s
b	o	l	d				c
	b	o	l	t			r
s	c	o	l	d		c	o
	t	o	l	l		o	l
p	o	l	l			l	l
j	o	l	t			t	
	m	o	l	t			

Fix the Word – page 96

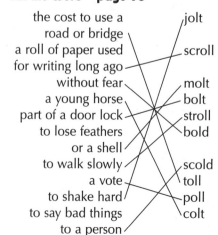

the cost to use a road or bridge — jolt
a roll of paper used for writing long ago — scroll
without fear — molt
a young horse — bolt
part of a door lock — stroll
to lose feathers or a shell — bold
to walk slowly — scold
a vote — toll
to shake hard — poll
to say bad things to a person — colt

LESSON 25 – Progress Monitoring

On Your Own – page 100
stuff **gear**   drill **bore**
dirt **soil**   female horse **ma**
fearless **bold**   cut **shear**
extra **spare**   make noise **blare**
walk **stroll**   work **toil**
young horse **colt**   center **core**
stories **lore**   trap **snare**
damp **moist**   lift **hoist**

LESSON 26

Word Wise – page 101
1. stall
2. rind
3. waltz
4. bind
5. grind
6. halt
7. post
8. squall
9. mild
10. host

Word Meaning
1. squall
2. post
3. mild
4. grind
5. waltz
6. host
7. rind
8. halt
9. stall
10. bind

Word by Word – page 102
1. stall
2. post
3. halt
4. bind
5. squall
6. waltz
7. grind
8. host
9. rind
10. mild

Word Find – page 103
Answers may vary. All of the words listed except **mild**.

In Your Own Words
Answers may vary.

Word Scramble – page 104
1. waltz
2. host
3. mild
4. halt
5. post
6. rind
7. bind
8. stall
9. grind
10. squall

LESSON 27

Word Wise – page 105
1. thigh
2. fraught
3. plight
4. flight
5. freight
6. sight
7. ought
8. sleigh
9. sigh
10. sought

Word Meaning
1. ought
2. sought
3. plight
4. freight
5. sight
6. sigh
7. flight
8. fraught
9. sleigh
10. thigh

146

ANSWER KEY

LESSON 27 cont'd.

Word by Word – page 106
1. ought
2. sleigh
3. flight
4. sought
5. freight
6. plight
7. sight
8. thigh
9. fraught
10. sigh

Word Cross – page 107

a	s	i	g	h	t	f	t
p	l	i	g	h	t	r	n
d	o	u	g	h	t	a	i
v	b	u	g	h	n	u	g
c	o	i	t	h	i	g	h
s	l	e	i	g	h	h	r
f	r	e	i	g	h	t	o

Making Sense

sought/a/friend
freight/on/ships

ought/to/study
fraught/with/
problems

to/sigh/loudly
a/long/flight
pull/the/sleigh

in/a/plight
hurt/her/thigh
a/funny/sight

Word Quest– page 108
1. ought
2. sought
3. sight
4. fraught
5. sleigh
6. sigh
7. freight
8. thigh
9. flight
10. plight

LESSON 28

Word Wise – page 109
1. brief
2. shriek
3. siege
4. wield
5. tier
6. pier
7. yield
8. fierce
9. pierce
10. grief

Word Meaning
1. wield
2. shriek
3. fierce
4. pierce
5. grief
6. yield
7. tier
8. brief
9. siege
10. pier

Word by Word – page 110
1. pier
2. shriek
3. tier
4. yield
5. brief
6. grief
7. siege
8. wield
9. fierce
10. pierce

Missing Letter – page 111
1. pierce
2. tier
3. shriek
4. yield
5. fierce
6. siege
7. grief
8. wield
9. brief
10. pier

Opposites
1. yield
2. fierce
3. grief
4. brief
5. shriek

Word Quest – page 112
1. pier
2. siege
3. fierce
4. yield
5. pierce
6. wield
7. brief
8. tier
9. shriek
10. grief

LESSON 29

Word Wise – page 113
1. vein
2. prey
3. rein
4. tread
5. reign
6. dread
7. stealth
8. realm
9. feign
10. veil

Word Meaning
1. dread
2. veil
3. realm
4. tread
5. prey
6. rein
7. stealth
8. feign
9. vein
10. reign

Word by Word – page 114
1. rein
2. feign
3. realm
4. vein
5. dread
6. prey
7. tread
8. reign
9. stealth
10. veil

Which One? – page 115
1. stealth
2. feign
3. vein
4. rein
5. realm

Word Maze

s	t	e	a	l	t	h	
	r	e	i	n			t
v	e	i	n		m	p	d	r
			l			r	r	e
i		a			e	e	a
l		e			y	a	d
	r	e	i	g	n		d
		f	e	i	g	n	

Fix the Word – page 116

strap to control a horse — rein
animal hunted by another animal — prey
to walk on and crush — tread
cloth worn over the head or face — veil
part of the body that carries blood — vein
to feel afraid — dread
quietly or secretly — stealth
to pretend — feign
area ruled by a king or queen — realm
time a king or queen rules — reign

LESSON 30 – Progress Monitoring

On Your Own – page 120
dance **waltz**
fear **dread**
storm **squall**
short **brief**
violent **fierce**
full of **fraught**
looked for **sought**
stop **halt**

pretend **feign**
layer **tier**
sadness **grief**
give up **yield**
scream **shriek**
hunted animal **prey**
tie **bind**
sled **sleigh**

LESSON 31

Word Wise – page 121
1. marshy
2. foamy
3. fuzzy
4. drafty
5. grumpy
6. chilly
7. quirky
8. witty
9. thrifty
10. messy

Word Meaning
1. witty
2. thrifty
3. chilly
4. grumpy
5. foamy
6. fuzzy
7. messy
8. quirky
9. drafty
10. marshy

Word by Word – page 122
1. grumpy
2. messy
3. thrifty
4. chilly
5. foamy
6. witty
7. drafty
8. fuzzy
9. marshy
10. quirky

Word Find – page 123
All of the words listed except drafty, foamy, grumpy.

In Your Own Words
Answers may vary.

ANSWER KEY

LESSON 31 cont'd.

Word Scramble – page 124
1. quirky
2. fuzzy
3. grumpy
4. thrifty
5. drafty
6. messy
7. foamy
8. marshy
9. witty
10. chilly

LESSON 32

Word Wise – page 125
1. swerved
2. merged
3. crouched
4. swooped
5. pared
6. hoisted
7. pierced
8. grieved
9. squirmed
10. bawled

Word Meaning
1. grieved
2. merged
3. crouched
4. bawled
5. swerved
6. pierced
7. hoisted
8. swooped
9. squirmed
10. pared

Word by Word – page 126
1. pared
2. bawled
3. hoisted
4. pierced
5. swerved
6. crouched
7. merged
8. squirmed
9. swooped
10. grieved

Word Cross – page 127

g	p	i	e	r	c	e	d	i
r	c	w	p	a	r	e	d	s
i	r	s	y	n	t	o	s	q
e	o	u	w	s	v	f	w	u
v	u	r	i	e	d	l	o	i
e	c	o	l	i	r	o	o	r
d	h	a	e	k	f	v	p	m
m	e	r	g	e	d	t	e	e
h	d	b	a	w	l	e	d	d

Making Sense
the/baby/bawled
grieved/about/it
cars/merged/
    carefully
pierced/her/ears

a/bird/swooped

hoisted/the/log
he/pared/potatoes
she/crouched/
    down
the/puppy/
    squirmed
a/driver/swerved

Word Swap – page 128
1. merged
2. pierced
3. grieved
4. bawled
5. squirmed
6. hoisted
7. swooped
8. swerved
9. pared
10. crouched

LESSON 33

Word Wise – page 129
1. plainly
2. mildly
3. nightly
4. meekly
5. firmly
6. faintly
7. briefly
8. boldly
9. glumly
10. deftly

Word Meaning
1. mildly
2. faintly
3. deftly
4. meekly
5. glumly
6. boldly
7. briefly
8. plainly
9. nightly
10. firmly

Word by Word – page 130
1. nightly
2. faintly
3. boldly
4. firmly
5. meekly
6. plainly
7. briefly
8. glumly
9. mildly
10. deftly

Missing Letter – page 131
1. deftly
2. faintly
3. mildly
4. plainly
5. briefly
6. glumly
7. nightly
8. firmly
9. meekly
10. boldly

Opposites
1. nightly
2. mildly
3. glumly
4. briefly
5. faintly

Word Quest – page 132
1. briefly
2. glumly
3. faintly
4. mildly
5. boldly
6. nightly
7. meekly
8. deftly
9. plainly
10. firmly

LESSON 34

Word Wise – page 133
1. shelves
2. calves
3. thieves
4. halves
5. scarves
6. loaves
7. elves
8. knives
9. leaves
10. hooves

Word Meaning
1. knives
2. leaves
3. elves
4. hooves
5. shelves
6. thieves
7. scarves
8. halves
9. calves
10. loaves

Word by Word – page 134
1. thieves
2. knives
3. loaves
4. shelves
5. leaves
6. calves
7. hooves
8. halves
9. elves
10. scarves

Which One? – page 135
1. shelves
2. hooves
3. scarves
4. elves
5. calves

Word Maze

c	a	l	v	e	s	s	s
e	l	v	e	s		c	h
h	o	o	v	e	s	a	e
k	n	i	v	e	s	r	l
l	e	a	v	e	s	v	v
l	o	a	v	e	s	e	e
h	a	l	v	e	s	s	s
t	h	i	e	v	e	s	

Fix the Word – page 136

young cows or bulls — calves
cloth worn around the neck — scarves
feet of a horse or deer — hooves
cutting tools — knives
shapes in which bread is baked — loaves
parts of a tree — leaves
magical people — elves
people who steal things — thieves
the tops of houses — rooves
boards on which things are stored — shelves

LESSON 35 – Progress Monitoring

On Your Own – page 140
flew down **swooped**
cold **chilly**
turned quickly **swerved**
smart **witty**
joined **merged**
breezy **drafty**
swampy **marshy**
simply **plainly**
became sad **grieved**
without fear **boldly**
strange **quirky**
cried **bawled**
lifted **hoisted**
unhappy **glumly**
gently **mildly**
not neat **messy**

RESEARCH BASIS OF *HIGH NOON VOCABULARY*

High Noon Vocabulary was developed using the results of a number of research studies as well as the recommendations of *The Report of the National Reading Panel: Teaching Children to Read* (2000). The five principles below reflect the most relevant research and recommendations of the National Reading Panel.

1. Vocabulary should be taught both directly and indirectly.
2. Repetition and multiple exposures to vocabulary items are important.
3. Learning in rich contexts is valuable for vocabulary learning.
4. Vocabulary learning should entail active engagement in learning tasks.
5. A variety of learning methods rather than dependence on a single method will optimize students' acquisition of new words and the skills needed to derive the meaning of words encountered in reading.

The Report of the National Reading Panel: Teaching Children to Read. (2000) Washington, DC: National Institute of Child Health and Human Development.

Rationale for emphasis on decoding

Thus, a first recommendation to educators who want to improve students' comprehension skills is to teach them to decode well...Word-recognition skills must be developed to the point of fluency if comprehension benefits are to be maximized.

Rationale for asserting the relationship between vocabulary and comprehension

It is well established that good comprehenders tend to have good vocabularies...a good case can be made that when students are taught vocabulary in a thorough fashion, their comprehension of what they read improves.

Pressley, M. "Comprehension instruction: What makes sense now, what might make sense soon." *Reading Online*, 5(2). September 2001, <http://www.readingonline.org/articles/art_index.asp?HREF=/articles/handbook/pressley/index.html>.

Rationale for grouping words with similar characteristics in each lesson

"...students with disabilities clustered words by categorical membership (i.e., semantically, phonemically, and structurally) less well than students without disabilities. Also, students with disabilities did less well than students without disabilities in activating word features from semantic memory to match the demands of a task."

Swanson, H.L. "Do semantic memory deficiencies underlie learning readers' encoding processes? *Journal of Experimental Child Psychology*, 4(1986), pp. 461–488.

Rationale for the use of "context rich" activities

With both groups, more target words were recalled when the deeper-level cues were used (i.e., target word embedded in a sentence versus rhyming pair), especially when the target word made sense semantically.

Walker, S.C., & J.A. Poteet. "Influencing memory performance in learning disabled students through semantic processing." *Learning Disabilities Research*, 5 (1) (1989), 25–32.

Rationale for teaching students to use strategies to derive meaning

Vocabulary instruction must move beyond the teaching of words directly as a primary activity. Because students derive the meanings of many words incidentally, without instruction, another possible role of instruction is to enhance the strategies readers use when they do in fact learn words incidentally. Directly teaching such strategies holds the promise of helping students become better independent word learners.

Kame'enui, E., D.W. Dixon & D. Carnine. "Issues in the design of vocabulary instruction." In *The nature of vocabulary acquisition,* edited by M.G. McKeown & M. E. Curtis. Hillsdale, NJ: Erlbaum, 1987.

Baker, S., D. Simmons & E. Kame'enui. "Vocabulary Acquisition: Synthesis of the Research." Eugene, OR: National Center to Improve the Tools of Educators, n.d. <http://idea.uoregon.edu/~ncite/documents/techrep/tech13.html>

Rationale for frequent, distributed practice

As we encounter a word repeatedly, more and more information accumulates about that word until we have a vague notion of what it "means." As we get more information, we are able to define that word.

Stahl, S. "Words Are Learned Incrementally Over Multiple Exposures." *American Educator,* Spring 2003. <http://www.aft.org/pubs-reports/american_educator/spring2003/stahl.html>. Adapted from Stahl, Steven. *Vocabulary Development.* From Reading Research to Practice: a Series for Teachers, vol. 2. Brookline, MA: Brookline Books, 1998.

UNDERSTANDING PROGRESS MONITORING

Progress monitoring is an assessment practice in which students' behaviors are measured on a regular basis. The goal of progress monitoring is to compare expected and actual student growth in order to determine the effectiveness of instruction and to make changes as necessary.

The graph below is an example of what a completed progress monitoring graph will look like when it is based on the periodic assessments in *High Noon Vocabulary*. Note that the example, the trajectory of scores is not continuously upward. Some students may make continuous upward progress, but others will not. Given the students for whom *High Noon Vocabulary* is intended, there is no typical pattern of progress. Moreover, it may be difficult to determine what expected progress should be. Even so, progress monitoring can provide useful information about students' decoding and vocabulary skills.

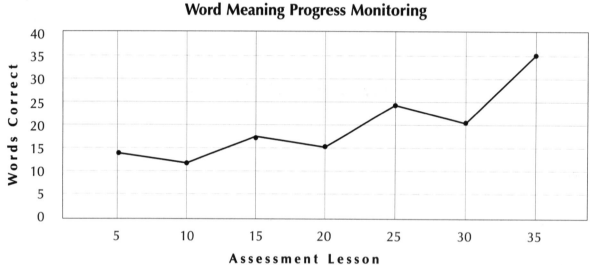

Word Meaning Progress Monitoring

If students' decoding and vocabulary skills are improving, the graph of their performance on the progress monitoring assessments should trend upward. This trend might not be apparent for several assessmentsr. In the example above, the trend doesn't move upward until the third assessment. For this reason, it is important to follow the program of instruction and complete the progress monitoring assessments. The pre- and posttests for each lesson can supplement the progress monitoring assessments and provide information about the short-term effects of instruction.

If a student is not making expected progress, the graph will show no overall growth and perhaps even a downward trend. When this happens, there are a number of steps to take.

- Begin using the pre- and posttests if you have not been doing so already. Using the pre- and posttests will provide timely information about the specific sound/spellings that might be causing difficulty.
- If you have not used the pretests regularly, administer them for lessons that have already been completed. The results of the assessment may point out the specific sound/spellings that the students haven't learned.
- Note the difference between the student's ability to decode the words and recall their meanings. If a discrepancy exists, focus on the weaker skill during the lesson activities.
- Evaluate the fidelity with which the program is being used. Be sure that the student understands the tasks, is completing the activities on a regular basis, and is experiencing the oral interaction needed to master the decoding and vocabulary skills that are featured in each lesson.

- Consider working with the student on an individual basis if you are not doing so already. Observe the student completing the activities and provide whatever assistance is needed for the student to complete them.
- For the activities in which the student is expected to read along, have the student read out loud with you.
- While the student is completing the items, or immediately after, have the student engage in a "think aloud" and explain how she or he found the answer. During the process prompt the student to read the lesson words. If necessary, practice blending the word sounds with the student.

Goal-setting is normally one of the early stages of progress monitoring. With students who are reading well below grade level, however, it might not be appropriate to establish goals without identifying patterns of reading behavior. Our recommendation is to have students complete at least fifteen lessons, including the progress monitoring assessments, in order to determine what are reasonable expectations.

With the two assessments that constitute progress monitoring in *High Noon Vocabulary*, students should increase both the number of words they can read correctly in one minute and the number of words they can define. The percentage gain will vary from student to student, and in the case of some students, it may increase dramatically once they develop automaticity. We recommend that you establish reasonable goals that match the abilities and needs of individual students. The goals should promote a sense of achievement in the student and be understandable to the significant adults in the student's life.

NameDate

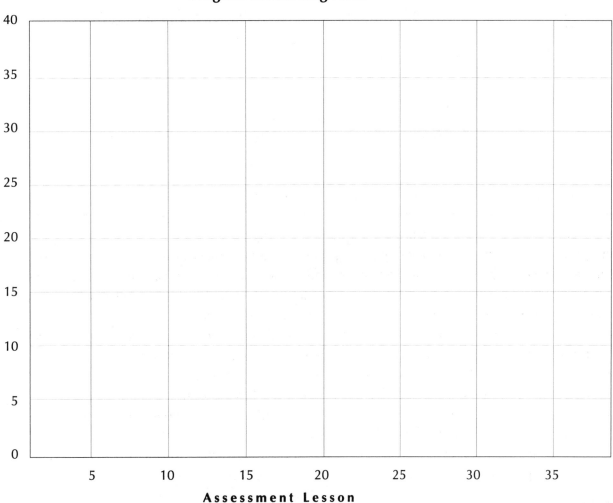

Progress Monitoring Form

Student Name _____ **Grade** _____

LESSON	DATE	PRETEST		POSTTEST	
		Word Recognition	Word Meaning	Word Recognition	Word Meaning
1	_____	_____	_____	_____	_____
2	_____	_____	_____	_____	_____
3	_____	_____	_____	_____	_____
4	_____	_____	_____	_____	_____

5	_____	Word Recognition _____	Word Meaning _____

6	_____	_____	_____	_____	_____
7	_____	_____	_____	_____	_____
8	_____	_____	_____	_____	_____
9	_____	_____	_____	_____	_____

10	_____	Word Recognition _____	Word Meaning _____

11	_____	_____	_____	_____	_____
12	_____	_____	_____	_____	_____
13	_____	_____	_____	_____	_____
14	_____	_____	_____	_____	_____

15	_____	Word Recognition _____	Word Meaning _____

16	_____	_____	_____	_____	_____
17	_____	_____	_____	_____	_____
18	_____	_____	_____	_____	_____
19	_____	_____	_____	_____	_____

20	_____	Word Recognition _____	Word Meaning _____

21	_____	_____	_____	_____	_____
22	_____	_____	_____	_____	_____
23	_____	_____	_____	_____	_____
24	_____	_____	_____	_____	_____

25	_____	Word Recognition _____	Word Meaning _____

26	_____	_____	_____	_____	_____
27	_____	_____	_____	_____	_____
28	_____	_____	_____	_____	_____
29	_____	_____	_____	_____	_____

30	_____	Word Recognition _____	Word Meaning _____

31	_____	_____	_____	_____	_____
32	_____	_____	_____	_____	_____
33	_____	_____	_____	_____	_____
34	_____	_____	_____	_____	_____

35	_____	Word Recognition _____	Word Meaning _____